# TWISTING THE TAIL OF
# THE DRAGON

# TWISTING THE TAIL OF THE DRAGON

*Jean Mathers*

*The Book Guild Ltd*
*Sussex, England*

*I sincerely hope David and Jessie enjoy this story of humour and horror. Myrtle's patient help has been invaluable as have the gallant friends involved in the seemingly endless years of Banzai.*

The Book Guild Limited
25 High Street
Lewes, Sussex

First published 1994
© Jean Mathers 1994

Set in Baskerville

Typesetting by Dataset
St Leonards-on-Sea, Sussex

Printed in Great Britain by
Antony Rowe Ltd
Chippenham, Wiltshire

A catalogue record for this book is
available from the British Library

ISBN 0 86332 966 7

# PROLOGUE

As early as the outbreak of war in Europe the Hong Kong Government, mindful of the impending attack on the colony by the Japanese, decided to evacuate all wives and children of the civil servants – and in fact suggested to the local and international companies that women in non-essential posts during a time of war, be likewise evacuated. A massive governmental scheme was launched to this effect. Many of the large Hongs followed Government advice. Although a few non-government wives without children returned, the evacuation did mean that there were relatively few young families caught as hostages of war when Japan finally invaded Hong Kong.

This is my story of life in Stanley Internment Camp, Hong Kong from January 1942 until late August 1945. The characters are real fellow internees. Some of the names are products of my imagination. The facts are here but inevitably the circumstances and surroundings have encouraged fantasy to enter naturally into some of the situations. The bulk of us arrived at the camp by boat from the Macau Ferry Pier on the north side of Hong Kong Island, past Green Island, Aberdeen, thence to the south-west point of Stanley, disembarking on one of our pre-war pleasure spots of Stanley beach. January 20 and 21, 1942, the main load of internees were ferried ashore. On January 30 a group of about ninety-six men, women and children arrived from St Paul's College where they had been living since the surrender. These were followed in the second week of February by a large number of residents from the Peak, plus another group from the University. It wasn't until August of 1942 that the last of our people living outside the camp were finally interned, approximately ninety-six nurses who had been at their posts nursing the sick and wounded by permission of the Japanese. After the January 20 and 21 shore landings the remainder of the groups were driven into camp by lorries. Some were fortunate enough to be able to bring a few of their possessions with them.

Over the three years and eight months of internment the average population of the camp was officially given as 2,500 plus about 106 children under the age of three. In fact the numbers varied from a maximum of 2,860 in April of 1942 to 2,400 in August 1945. Our numbers consisted of roughly 2,325 British, about 290 American citizens, and 60 odd Dutch and Belgians. The Americans were repatriated in July of 1942 and the Canadians, who were classified as British on arrival at the camp, were repatriated in September 1943. In May of 1942 a small band of residents from Shanghai, caught in Hong Kong during the hostilities, requested and were granted repatriation to Shanghai. They were of different nationalities who, though not strangers to Hong Kong, preferred to take their chances in their own city of Shanghai.

So here we were, friends, families and strangers

herded together into a totally unknown future but all passionately committed to the same goal – survival. Our absorption in how to achieve that goal was priority number one in the years to follow. Inevitably ethics did not always take pride of place. However in general the assessment of our situation was that loyalty to each other and to those selected by the majority to safeguard our interests must be fiercely guarded. The undecided day-to-day behaviour of our captors during the early days of setting up the internment camp naturally created apprehension and uncertainty, and it was therefore important that there be no warring factions within the camp. A difficult situation to contain with the diversity of peoples and positions of value in their pre-camp lives.

As adjustments were made, the greatest daily threat was boredom. The humdrummery of communal living with its barely visible veneer of civilised behaviour was aggravated by lack of privacy which, for years treated with familiarity, became a very special commodity. Then there were the two new enemies – weather and the real gut-ache of hunger which had not in the past presented a vital threat. Constant cold through that first winter made sorry figures of us – red runny noses, chapped hands, chilblains. Dysentery was rife through the camp, where the shortage of water and the crowded sanitary arrangements, made it impossible to eradicate. Beri-beri was also quite common.

The main anxiety, which remained throughout the years, was the welfare of our men over the harbour in the camps in Kowloon. News was very sketchy and mostly bad in those early months. The long hours of darkness with the short evenings and lack of proper lighting exacerbated the intense physical longing for the love and intimacy of our lovers, husbands and fathers. Many liaisons started innocently with this need and hunger for natural feelings to be released. Some of these liaisons resulted in heartbreak for everyone involved. There were, however, compensations in the warmth of friendship. Endless and dreary daily chores had to be got through, and were relieved usually by being shared. There were the news vendors – whispers real or rumoured, victories outside our world of dreaded disasters. Plans for life after our release occupied a generous slice of our conversation. Allied victory was never in the distant future, but always just a very brief time away. The prophets of doom were given short shrift.

There must be many stories of those frustrating years for others to tell, who like myself, ultimately converted the goal of survival into Freedom, the most precious of man's civilised gifts. The wonderment that life was beginning after a long hibernation! The deep compassion for those fellow internees who could not join in the thankfulness of peace on earth. That miraculous sensation in true form chased and destroyed the fear and anguish pent up during the darkest shadows of the years of captivity.

Jean Mathers

# 1

On Friday, December 5 1941 my life changed, although I was not aware of it at the time. A telephone call came from my husband to say he had leave from 4p.m. on Saturday until the same time on Sunday.

His company was stationed on the frontier, and we had not seen each other for two weeks. As we had only been married for three months his colonel tried to be as generous as the situation allowed, for brief visits. I was the only regimental wife in Hong Kong, and as such could not expect privileges. A Saturday leave was a welcome bonus. A carefree night with friends dining and dancing at the famous Gripps.

Since Britain's declaration of war on Hitler's battle-hungry hordes, we had, in Hong Kong, been slowly preparing for our eventual part in the holocaust. The Air Raid Precaution Service was instituted, building air raid shelters and pillboxes completed. There were endless fund-raising activities for Bombers for Britain.

In 1939 the government services, and many local companies as well as international companies decided to evacuate the women and children for whom they were responsible. Australia and North America were the two countries to which these evacuees were sent.

Women in the essential services were given the choice of leaving the colony, or remaining at their posts as their husbands or consciences dictated.

The European theatre of war, although so remote from our lives, seemed to produce a euphoric state of subconscious breath-holding. We were afraid the beautiful bubble of normality would burst. Inevitably the Japanese armies, now on our boundary, would attack both land and shore to challenge our supremacy.

So it was that on the night of Saturday, December 6 the bubble burst. Whilst the Gripps was swinging with gay parties, and couples dancing to the tune of 'My Heart Belongs To Daddy', the music stopped. The band gave a thunderous roll on the drums, which was followed by a firm voice announcing over the microphone that: ALL SERVICE PERSONNEL MILITARY NAVAL AND MERCANTILE MUST RETURN TO THEIR UNITS IMMEDIATELY.

The hush was almost like a sigh of relief. The two years on the carousel were over. The band struck up a rousing 'God Save The King'. The Gripps and the glasses emptied. Those few with no units to rejoin ordered the ever welcome 'one for the road'.

On Monday December 8, 5a.m. Joyce, my long-time friend, and a senior secretary at Government Battle Headquarters in the city of Victoria on the island of Hong Kong, telephoned and in a breathless voice announced that the Japanese were attacking.

As Air Raid Precaution Warden in charge of personnel in Kowloon, my first duty was to round up our members for transportation to ARP HQ, on the Island.

The government van allocated to me for this purpose, was waiting with a driver outside my flat.

Final pick-up being at Kai Tak airport. As we had no aircraft for defence, a fact of which I assumed Japanese intelligence to be aware, we did not expect any aerial activity. Lesson One, do not assume!

The airfield was not in fact under attack, but one nastly little Japanese job was making determined passes at the runway and the parked vehicles. The main target which the pilot was teasing, with a view no doubt to a spectacular unloading of his bombs, was the pride of Pan Am Airways. Hove-to alongside the jetty at Kai Tak was the new Pan Am clipper, ready to return to the United States after her triumphant inaugural flight to the Far East. Her passenger list resembled a page from Debrett! Although the passengers had no way of knowing at the time, most were evacuated with the Americans when the June repatriation took place. Not too far from the van we could hear voices shouting at us to come over and take cover and there was much arm-waving from what appeared to be a ditch along the perimeter of the field. The seven of us shot across to the signallers, who in turn heaved us down into what turned out to be an open sewer!

If you have to conquer an all-engulfing fear the antidote is anger. To have the curtain go up on Act One of your war, and find yourself ankle deep in shit, the slow burn becomes a conflagration! In a fury I sloshed my way through unspeakables towards the entrance to the airport, where there had to be an exit out of this ignominity. Climbing out, all the gutter language I was capable of spewing acted as a pacemaker back to my flat.

Our little amah, Ah Foon, was leaning over the balcony from where she had a grandstand view of the airport. I yelled at her to come down the back stairs with a bucket of hot water, disinfectant and several bath towels. In the back yard I removed my uniform trousers, shoes etc., while Ah Foon sluiced me down before I shot up the short flight of back stairs to the flat, a hot shower and scrub.

At this point my mother telephoned me to say that she was watching the RAF practice bombing Kai Tak!

I had not had time to contact Mother and warn her that our particular war was now a reality after so very many false alarms. However, this was the moment to disenchant her as to the mission of the lone aircraft, and persuade her to come over to my flat with her amah, Ah Kwai. At least we would be together as and when I was off-duty.

By the morning of Thursday, December 11 Wang Ching Wei's group had infiltrated into Kowloon. Mother had moved into my flat. Ready to make my way over to ARP HQ I sensed a sudden absence of the usual street noises and traffic movement around us. Just as suddenly the front door was kicked in and a very tall Chinese gentleman in a long dark blue gown appeared. Behind him, brandishing various pieces of armoury were a tribe of khaki-clad, rubber-booted, ferocious-looking soldiers. Ah Foon, roughly handled by an identical gang, was thrust into the room from the kitchen, rigid with fright.

The tall Chinese identified himself as the officer in charge, and asked me in perfect English, whether there were any servicemen on the premises. Thankful that Badshadin, David's orderly, had left for Regimental HQ about ten minutes before, I was able to tell the truth, as his khaki boys were nervous and on the rampage. They proceeded to search the rooms, overturning furniture in their way, and generally vandalising my home into a junk heap.

At this point Mother decided it was time she took charge. In her Irish brogue, which penetrates in great moments of passion, she loudly threatened the tall Chinese with fearsome reprisals from Mr Churchill when he was informed of the atrocity.

At first I thought I detected a smile hovering round the leader's lips. Not so. There was an instant hush, the rabble realising their officer was about to speak. The tall Chinese ignored Mother, and turning to me literally spat sibilantly at me to 'leave at once with the other two before I lose my temper!'

The crowds we joined were surging towards the Ferry Pier. The three of us clung together, which was not too easy with a frenzied crowd elbowing and shoving. Halfway down the road to the Ferry Pier there were barricades guarded by British troops, trying their utmost to control the masses and, at the same time avert a panic. It was a hazardous and frightening voyage across the harbour, crammed with craft plying their overloaded decks with people hoping to find refuge on the Island from the oncoming Japanese army – two rather small fighter airplanes were buzzing the sea at junks, sampans, small yachts and ferries. There were some casualties but their main object appeared to be to show their supremacy, and not to slaughter; otherwise they could have sunk the lot, creating a dreadful waterway of carnage. One of David's brother officers was O.C. Ferry, and played a magnificent part in calming the passengers. I was able to get belated news that David and his men were still holding their positions as they planned their route to the Island by dark.

Our much overloaded ferry docked quickly and safely at the Island Pier. Mother and Ah Foon set off for Joyce's flat in Queen's Road, where we were

13

expected in the event of a Kowloon evacuation. I got myself off to ARP HQ, not in uniform but in slacks and sweater. This, I realised later, had helped our hasty departure from the flat. A uniform would have been very provoking to our uninvited guests! Later that night after duty, I made my way back to Joyce's home. The streets were palely lit with the odd lamp. Not too many people about; a few rickshaws jog-trotted past; a traffic policeman still on point duty at the crossroads. The nightmare of the previous hours was still vivid. The date, Thursday December 11, was, I realised, three months to the day that we had got married and had spent that carefree happy day with our friends.

Time was mercifully too short for me to be sentimentally involved with our possessions. Nevertheless I was tingling with fury at the debris that had been left behind in my new home and the horror of this first encounter with barbarity brought on the shakes. Across the road I spotted a dimly lit noodle stall doing a roaring trade. Customers were clustered together, slurping up the comforting warm contents of their bowls. There were a few coins in my pocket so I happily joined the gang. They were remarkably cheerful, filthy remarks about the Japanese being the main topic of conversation. A bowl and chopsticks were deftly passed to me through the crowd, who were anxious to know if I had any late information on the progress of the hostilities. As small groups drifted off and others took their places I gradually got enough control of myself to join the family at Joyce's flat.

The news was not very encouraging. Kowloon was being evacuated of foreign residents, and of those locals who could make their way over to the Island if they so wished together with the forces which had been ordered to retreat to continue their stand.

Reports from other parts of South East Asia were disheartening. There was certainly no hope of reinforcements from the outside. Our defence was savage, the final analysis alarmingly obvious.

Joyce's flat was to be evacuated the following day. Mother and I had been billeted on The Peak. Ah Foon preferred to remain with her people in the city. The house on The Peak was occupied by a company of Canadian soldiers, to whom we were an obvious embarrassment, along with four other women. My post for duty had been altered to the tunnel under Government House, where along with ARP personnel a first aid post had been set up to look after any nearby casualties. The first morning I was able to get a lift down to the tunnel. The day was hectic. Aircraft were buzzing about the skies, indiscriminately dropping their bombs at will. However, it was clear that they had no intention of reducing the centre of the city, nor the dockyard and other public facilities, to rubble. These would be needed after their victory. By night they loosed off the odd mortar bomb, no doubt hoping to panic the population. A minor Dunkirk was planned to take our men off the mainland, with as much armoury as could be rescued.

Getting back to The Peak that evening was pretty frightening, but a band of us managed to climb on a lorry going up the hill, and were dropped off as near as possible to our billets. Several platoons of Japanese had already got a foothold on the Island, and with the information they were being signalled, knew where most of our military positions were. The atmosphere at our evening meal was tense. The officer in charge explained that the Japanese were preparing to launch an attack on his position, and if possible, arrangements must be made to get the six of us out early next morning.

During the night Joyce rang up from Government Headquarters to say that the six of us must be ready at dawn when she would collect us by car. At first light the usual spotter aircraft, always on time and known as Charlie Boy, made his first sortie over the Island, turning and dipping, sending down a bomb or two for good measure. Having said our farewells, good luck and God speed to our Canadian hosts, we huddled by the gate to watch for the car. Joyce, true to her word, arrived in a commandeered car with driver. The driver slowed down enough for us to scramble in before speeding down the road. It was an extremely brave rescue. If it had not succeeded we would have been overrun with those gallant Canadians that very night.

Most of the remnants of the Kowloon residents were now occupying rooms in the Gloucester Hotel, where we joined them. Despite a certain amount of gloom and bewilderment, most of us appeared at our particular battle stations.

As soon as we were sorted out, and settled in a room together, I trundled up to the tunnel where there was much to be done. The first news given me was that David was still alive, safely on the Island with his men, and still fighting.

In our underground bunker it was not easy to hear the cacophony of heavy gunfire and bombing, but the earth tremors told us that the enemy was firing pretty accurately. I was in the office with Joyce when one of my ARP personnel came in with tears filling her eyes, to tell me that about thirty Indian soldiers had been brought into the tunnel. They had just been bombed while taking up positions at the junction of the main road Most of them had suffered horrific wounds, and were begging for water. I went to speak to them and realised they were part of David's company – together with an assortment of British lads who were separated from their group.

First aid was being administered as quickly as possible, whilst ambulances were called up to take them to the military hospital across the valley. For most of them it was too late, but I managed to get the Indian troops' numbers, so that at least HQ would have a record. A St John's Ambulance man was looking after the British casualties and I learned much later that a very small number had survived.

It was my first-hand introduction to the horrors of war; the tragic picture was in my mind for the rest of the day, and during that sleepless night I wondered if I would ever forget the whimpers of agony, the smell of blood, vomit, fear, and the shame that my foremost thought was that we were so lucky that David was not amongst those men of his.

We knew that there had been a demand for surrender by the Japanese, which had been stubbornly rejected. It was not a case of could we hold out, but for how long, before the Island was forcibly taken with horrific loss of civilian life. Hong Kong at this time had a multiracial multinational population with refugees from different parts of the world overcrowding our very limited territory. Our water supply was off as the Japanese had cut the Island in two. Already there were countless cases of dysentery flooding the overcrowded hospitals. The terrible decision had to be taken. The second and last demand by the Japanese commander was made. Our Commander-in-Chief had no alternative but to accept.

17

*Christmas Day, 1941 – Surrender.*

The humiliating message was broadcast to the people, adding that we must remain where we were, or if possible get back to our homes and await further orders. Returning to the hotel was a traumatic experience: Chinese hurrying back to their families, the odd European like myself getting back to base, all with total disbelief blanketing our faces.

All hotel 'guests' were told to be in the dining room by eight the next morning when we would be given breakfast. Andrew, a senior civil servant, would explain what was happening, and try to keep us up-to-date as to our next movements.

The night was lost in hideous speculation. We visited each others' rooms to find out if anyone had news of their fighting men. The Chinese room-boys were helpfully handing out tins or bottles of beer. There was precious little water left in the hotel tanks. Everyone was trying to get a quick wash, before the supply ran out – cleaning one's teeth in warm beer is not to be recommended! The city sounded ominously filled with the alien tramping of feet, sporadic shouts and shots. Most of us were remarkably dry-eyed, unable to absorb the reality of surrender, or imagine the confusion of the immediate future.

On Boxing Day the large hotel dining room slowly filled with a stunned, and somewhat bedraggled looking lot of 'guests'. Nasty little soldiers bristling with bayonets, barking unintelligible orders, prodded us into chairs scattered around the tables. Two of these gallant victors stationed themselves at our table for six. One was behind Mother and I. That sinking feeling hit my tummy as, glancing at Mother, I could sense that any moment she was about to expand once again on what our Mr Churchill's vengeance would be. Covering her hand tightly I managed to growl 'QUIET PLEASE'. Mother got the message, as she almost knocked her cup of rapidly cooling tea over a plate of already soggy bread positioned at our end of the table. Reprieve!

Andrew, calm and reassuring, told us that negotiations were underway as to where to intern the civilian population prior, he hoped, to repatriation. In the meantime we would be housed in Chinese hotels and boarding houses which abounded in the centre of town. He quietly answered what questions he could. The services would assemble at Murray Parade Ground, from where they would be taken to camps over in Kowloon. All the civilian males needed to co-operate during the transitional period would be registered. He strongly advised us to remain in the hotel until he could give us further news.

My first thought was to make my way to Murray Parade Ground to see if I could get a glimpse of David and the rest of the boys. Quite a few of the 'guests' decided to do the same, and we set off together. The parade ground was not very far away, and hopefully there would be others milling towards it for the same reason. However, on our way we were told by one of our police that the assembly was not until the following day.

We were bitterly disappointed, but felt in fairness to Andrew we should return to the hotel in case there was further news. Joyce was sure to have the latest movements of the troops assembly, and perhaps we could make the short journey again tomorrow.

Happily, whilst on the way to the parade ground I met several of my friends whose homes were in Victoria. They were not too far from the city centre and as their homes were not damaged they were able to stay together. They also gave refuge to friends from the mainland. They were very generous in their offers to shelter Mother and I. However, I felt it was better that we stay at the hotel where Andrew knew we were to be easily found.

Back in the hotel there was quite a gathering in the room; mostly old chums wishing for news and company. We were able to scrounge food during the day, which dragged on with talk, talk and more talk. All manner of rumours, largely alarmist, were being discussed as the reality of the situation forced us to come to terms with what surrender implied in its present unknown future.

Around dusk there was a quick sharp rap on the door. The chattering stopped as I cautiously peered through an opened crack. Dear God, there was David, Andrew behind him. They came in quietly and hurriedly. David and I were in a bear-hug, holding each other fiercely. He looked so wonderful. Hugging everyone, he tried to remember messages he had been given to pass on. Andrew was nervous, saying that they must be off as quickly as possible. David asked me not to come to the assembly at the parade ground the next day. Mother had opened a bottle of beer for each of them, which they drank quickly and thirstily. Then came the falsely bright farewells. How heavenly it was to have been able to touch him! Only later when Andrew returned for a few minutes to tell me David was safely back in his quarters did I realise what a tremendously courageous act of friendship on Andrew's part it had been, bringing David to me. Had David been caught in uniform in the hotel, it would of course have meant instant execution for them both. With Andrew's presence, his official armband declaring him one of the highest officers in the administration under the Japanese Commander-in-Chief, there was at least a chance of protection had they been halted during their brief walk to and from the hotel.

Much later Andrew explained that during the chaos and confusion of the first few days it had not been too difficult to leave Battalion HQ which was in Garden Road, only a ten minute walk from the hotel. Knowing that I was longing to visit HQ to see everyone before they were shipped over to the camps in Kowloon, David had already explained to me in a brief note which he left with Mother to give me, that the CO had strictly forbidden any visiting – naturally. There was far too much to do and get ready before being separated from the men. Apart from those left in HQ it was almost impossible for the officers to see them to explain why they would not be able to be with their own company commanders. A harrowing experience for everyone. It was our turn to line up at Murray Parade Ground and the group from the hotel decided to stick together. It was like old home week on the parade ground! So many friends we had not seen since the beginning of the war. As it looked like a long wait before anyone would be on the march, we made ourselves as comfortable as possible, got out our smokes, and began with questions and answers! It was sad to hear of the death on the battlefield of so many companions from the good old days. Apparently St Paul's College was caring for a great number of wounded. Also a contingent of nurses were still at their posts in Kowloon. We heard of the horrors of Happy Valley, where other volunteers tending the wounded were caught in the height of battle on the Island.

This band of volunteer nurses were billeted in the

Jockey Club, near enough to St Paul's Hospital to be able to help the overcrowded hospital when needed. Unfortunately the Jockey Club was being used to help the lightly wounded and on their push into the Island the Japanese showed their usual bestial treatment of women, submitting them, despite their nurses' uniforms, to an orgy of rape and beatings. Thus these young women too became the casualties of war.

# 2

Eventually things began to stir. We were told to form lines, keeping as many members of the families as were present together. The older citizens were to be allowed to use rickshaws. Grabbing one for Mother we loaded our meagre bundles under her legs. It really was an incredible sight. Some of us couldn't help giggling at the incongruity of our position. The crocodiles started out of the gate, two of our men at the head, while guards heavily armed (they must have been madly uncomfortable) spread themselves down the ragged lines. Some wag started up 'It's a long way to Tipperary' but soon decided he had better keep his breath for the long march!

It must have been an awesome sight to see this long crocodile of polyglot men, women and children – by no means the entire foreign civilian population – being herded through the gates of the parade ground on their first march towards internment. This turned out to be one of the most gruelling marches we were to embark upon. There were more to come, but fortunately there was no time to speculate what was in store on that particular day – the worry-warts would have many opportunities to forecast gloom and doom!

Our first destination was Des Voeux Road, which

was thickly populated with Chinese hotels, boarding houses and brothels, mostly with restaurants on the ground floor.

It was a long, tiring and frightening day with endless tramping back and forth Des Voeux Road. Batches were sorted out by the Japanese officer in charge, who was accompanied by one of our police officers. These batches were either added to or cut down according to the availability of the various types of accommodation. The many stops we made became tedious, but gave us a chance to find something to drink. The Chinese population who were about, curious to know what was going on, were quite wonderful, coming forward with tasty bits to eat, fruit and bottles of fizzy drinks. Our guards by this time were as edgy and footsore as ourselves. More rickshaws were called up for the women carrying young children; the older children were fractious and had to be constantly gathered up and returned to their harrassed parents.

The crocodile was thinning out. Finally a large section of us were halted opposite a very smart-looking hotel. The front door grilles were slammed open, and to a rather ragged cheer we were prodded in. The proprietor, his family and staff welcomed us courteously. Their sympathy and shock at the invasion of such a dilapidated assortment of humanity soon turned to practicality. Endless brews of tea and bowls of rice were handed out and the sorting out of quarters began. Mother and two of our American friends were directed to a two-bunk cubicle, first floor front. A great advantage as the landing overlooked Des Voeux Road. I was doing a recce of the facilities, locating the sanitary arrangements, and discovering that the roof was laid out with tables and chairs for

24

eating. We were very lucky as our cubicle had a small wash basin, and water was still available. We had a quick face-splash, and leaving Mother to rest, the three of us went to see how the rest of our group were faring.

The following days were filled with sorting out ourselves and our environment. In the mornings there would be a surge of Chinese friends at the grille, all bringing packages to ease the burden, clothes, food and most welcome toilet articles. These visits were allowed for a brief period, and one happy morning I saw little Ah Foon's face, shining with tears. She had somehow been able to salvage a few pieces of essential clothing for us both, packed in a Hong Kong basket. She assured me that she was being looked after by cousins, and had brought me some money that Missie Joyce had given her for me. She scrabbled in her own little bundle, but the guard who had permitted the basket to be handed over, suddenly got in a towering fury when he saw the money. Hitting her savagely across the head he kicked her down on to the road, screaming for her to leave. The misery of watching that little soul, obviously hurt, crawl away and disappear into the jostling crowds, made us all sick with fear for her. The looks of bitter hatred on the faces of the hotel staff made one's blood freeze.

A few brave friends continued to visit, but only to hand out small gifts of fruit, what little money they could spare, cautiously whisper news of our men in the camps, and the odd message from Chinese friends still in Kowloon. Time passed in a glaze of discomfort. There were only rumours as to what or where the future would be. Our cubicles were haunted by unwanted nightly visitors! They came scuttling along the partitions, foraging in our bundles for scraps of food. Their beastly beady eyes would focus on us as we went to rescue whatever they were after, before they left screeching as someone got a direct hit with a shoe! We became expert at ratting, especially when they made off with our precious bits of soap left carelessly by the enamel basin.

Mother chummed up with a delightful woman of her own age from the next cubicle. Minnie and Mother would chat away over their bowls of morning tea, until Minnie would announce that she must dash to 'check on my girls'. Mother told me in a puzzled voice that Minnie had six 'girls' in the hotel. Four Australian, one French and a Persian! Could they all be by different husbands? But obviously! It was hard to believe that Mother could be so naive, but it did take her a lot of puzzling over, before she finally asked Minnie to explain the relationship!

We were not allowed out of the hotel, exercise being taken on the flat roof. Life was unreal. The important thing was to try and find ways of filling in time by perhaps helping with the children, or taking places in the food queues for the elderly who were unable to climb up the stairs to the 'dining room' to collect their rations. There was, of course, the cleaning of our quarters, and ourselves. Water was very strictly doled out. Every day one or more of our fellow guests were taken off to hospital suffering from skin or stomach disorders.

Communication between ourselves and the other places of confinement was sketchy. We had to rely on our morning visitors for news of them. However, this fraternisation was suddenly stopped. The spokesman for our hotel, Mr Stevens, a member of one of the older companies in the colony, suspected that this

26

meant news of our departure to the final destination must be very close.

He had been escorted by armed guard twice, to the offices of our Administration who were co-operating with the Japanese as to the safest site for an internment camp. Returning from his second visit he gathered us together on the roof, and told us that the site chosen was the Stanley Peninsula. Teams were already there on a mopping-up operation prior to our arrival. This was a mammoth task as the Stanley garrison, owing to a breakdown in communications, had not received the news of the capitulation until late on Boxing Day.

It was one of those ghastly misunderstandings. The Japanese were already in the Stanley Peninsula, making their way up to the garrison on the far end of the tip on a hill. Our troops, having no idea that the Commander-in-Chief had surrendered, continued to attack fiercely. This was when the hospital at Stanley, full of casualties, was subjected to acts of appalling atrocities as well as great heroism in the last two days of battle.

The Japanese were determined our death rattle would be as vicious as they could deliver. The hospital was attacked. The wounded were bayonetted in their beds; the doctor operating at the time was also bayonetted with his staff, as was the patient on the operating table. The nurses were violated during the two days and nights. Even condoning the 'heat of battle' surely such blood lust went beyond the ferocity of human imagining. The garrison from the hill were decimated (few were left alive as the Japanese do not take prisoners of war). When they themselves are mortally wounded they commit hari-kari, or so we were told, but at the end of the battle by us, for Hong

Kong, there were an amazing lot of healthy Japanese to be rounded up!

Mr Stevens offered to take urgent messages to the administration office which he was now visiting almost daily but he asked that they be brief. I had known that Joyce was one of the senior women staff working in the offices on the paperwork, so sent my urgent message, asking that if it was possible would she get in touch with Ah Foon to see that she was all right. Also, if possible, to give her whatever money Joyce had been holding for Mother and myself. The staff coped splendidly with most of the hundreds of enquiries and requests they must have been deluged with.

At long long last, on Mr Stevens' return from what turned out to be his final visit, he had our departure date for embarkation. This was to be from the Macau Ferry Pier East Point. Early on the morning of January 21, we were assembled outside our hotel. Our crocodile was formed, and way down the road on either side we could see sections of the civilians marked for Stanley camp. All traffic had been prohibited, except for the life-saving rickshaws, once again lined up to transport the old, sick, and this time most of the children.

Clutching the bundles, which had accumulated, the processions under armed guard, filed slowly down towards the pier. There was much ribaldry as the lines caught up with or passed other groups headed the same way. The usual marching songs were rivalled by lewd rugger ditties. There were shouts of 'Wot no Taxi' as the rickshaws passed, but underlying the forced jollity was a universal apprehension.

It was a lucky day for us that the Japanese Navy was in charge of the operation. The Navy were more understanding of Western ways. Many of their officers, we were told, had been through Dartmouth. Officers were detailed to man the pier, and deal with the loading of human cargo. Perhaps they would not be too unsympathetic to this next step on our way to Stanley Camp; we were leaving familiar landmarks and many friends behind, most being apprehensive of being cut off from Victoria. When a crocodile arrived our spokesman was summoned to stand alongside one of the Japanese officers, while his details were briefly processed and directed to their transport. As each boat was loaded to capacity she cast off amid advice from the remaining crowd: 'Remember your seasick pills', 'Keep to starboard' and the important 'Keep the pub open'. Even the kids joined in waving and cheering!

The guards were getting restless. However, the officers seemed quite unperturbed, and civil. The day was hotting up, exacerbated by very little shade to be found on the open concourse. There didn't appear to be any order of embarkation. As one load of passengers were away, another batch were lined up for the check out. The boats looked remarkably unsafe for the numbers trooping aboard. It was disturbing too, that most of the people were sent below. However, the sea was clear and calm, and it would be heavenly to feel the cool breeze, once underway.

As the morning wore into afternoon, the problems of toilet urgencies and thirst became acute. Most of us had brought bottles of water, but these were soon emptied. The two toilets which served the pier had a constant queue. Only the children were able to relieve themselves in the open, away from the main body of listless adults.

Nervous rumours were circulating that unless embarkation was completed before sundown, we would have to retrace our steps to the various hotels! The waterfront blocks were filled with curious Chinese leaning out of the windows, or watching from the roofs. Most of them tried to cheer us up by waving, or giving the good luck sign.

After what seemed forever our spokesman, Mr Stevens, was ordered to take up his position beside the officer on the left hand side of the barricade. Mother and I finally reached the barricade for our turn of processing. The officer was young and very arrogant, but he spoke reasonable English, as he asked Mr Stevens for the list from our hotel.

Mother first, name? Nationality? I couldn't believe it. Mother's Irish pride had surfaced. In her best Irish brogue, and the worst moment of my life, 'IRISH', announced Mother, loud and clear. The Japanese were not at war with Eire, so Ma was pushed out of line, behind the officer. A guard immediately appeared to take up his position beside her.

I had no choice, so without being summoned I stepped in front of the officer and desperately began explaining that my mother was British, as was I. She happened to have been born in Ireland. Mr Stevens was trying to stem the flow of explanations I was heaping upon the officer. Mother was disorientated by her recent experiences; she was sick, she had nowhere to go, she MUST stay with me. The officer was getting impatient. My next recollection was of a guard taking me firmly by the arm, lining me up beside Mother, and standing in front of us with his back to the crowd.

Memory does not recall how the end result was accomplished. We were apparently shoved on board almost at the last moment. I can only think that the anguish and urgency of my pleas got through to the young officer. It was his duty to get this rabble loaded and away; few of us had passports or means of identification. Obviously Mother and I created a complication where more vital ones existed, so the answer was on board and away.

When the chaos of getting billeted and documented in the camp had settled down Mr Stevens cleared up the mystery of how Mother and I were boarded on the ferry. He explained that the Japanese officer was in a quandary as to what to do with the pair of us, and actually appealed to Mr Stevens for his advice. This bewildered Mr Stevens so that he simply said he thought the only solution was to allow mother and daughter to continue with the original plan for all civilian residents to be taken to the Stanley Internment Camp. As I said to Mother, if that wasn't the luck of the Irish, which, *please*, she must never push to the limit ever again!

The next few hours were hardly a joy-ride. We were packed in below decks. The air was fetid, the boat was pitching and rolling. The children sensed the undercurrent of panic and responded with howls and screams for comfort. We were almost elbow to elbow. Many unfortunates were being seasick. The men realised that the hatch on top of the gangway to our quarters would have to be opened. One of them, who was able to speak and understand a little Japanese, thrust his way through and up the gangway, hammering on the hatch calling for the officer in charge. The hatch was raised, exposing a pair of khaki-covered, rubber-booted bandy legs. A rifle butt was slammed into the man's face, another across his right shoulder, sending him bloodied and sprawling

31

back into the crowd. Before the hatch could be replaced, another of the men clawed his way up, shouting in English for the officer in charge.

Miraculously an officer appeared, flanked by guards with their fixed bayonets, and screamed down the hatch to 'Get back'.

The hatch remained open, encircled by the armed guards. There was no further movement above. The panic quietly abated. The wounded lad was attended to as best we could, the children finally shushed. Mercy, we could breathe.

Our boat was slowing down. There were voices and movement on deck. We could hear the anchor chains, and feel the boat stop altogether. Then came the orders. We eventually all managed to emerge. We were anchored fairly close in shore, off one of Stanley Peninsula's beautiful beaches. The bay was dappled with small craft, sampans and rowing boats to take us off and shuttle us ashore. The beach was surging with arrivals being formed once more into groups, to be marched into the camp, which was not visible from the shoreline.

We were very low in the water, and there were many helping hands both from our men on the boat and those in the small craft. Being lowered over the side, the use of only one rather narrow gangway was a hazardous ending to the afternoon's sail.

The children were handled first, either squealing with delight or screeching with fright. The Japanese guards were beside themselves laughing at our antics to get aboard the small craft as they came alongside. Mother, who has always had an unhealthy regard for water transport, hung back for as long as she dared. However the officer demanded a speedier disembarkation. The guards got into the act, forcing us to the rails, and either bundling us over the side, or pushing us down the gangway, to the waiting craft. Mother could no longer prolong the ordeal and was expertly caught at the bottom of the gangway for the short row to the beach. So it was we joined other bands huddled together awaiting directions. It was an enormous relief to see the stern of our vessel disappearing out to sea. Another beginning.

Amazingly it was still light, and not nearly as late as I had thought. It was curious, too, how we all appeared to have accepted the sight of the armed guards everywhere. Whilst gazing around I recognised the houses on the hill above the coast road. We had often been guests at tennis and beach parties with the families who had lived there in happier times!

Down the slope to the beach came Andrew's familiar figure. We waved. He joined us, leading us to a queue already formed, to be taken to our quarters. It was a pretty weary pack of stragglers who plodded along behind Andrew, up the beach, across the road and on into the camp site.

On arrival in front of a complex of buildings, Andrew told us this was a dispersal point. Our own men acted as guides leading groups to various parts of the buildings. Andrew led Mother and me to a room on the first floor of a block, where he had commandeered two places for us. Leaving us he said that we must stay where we were, and that the next day we would be given the lay of the land.

There were four women already in the room, one of whom was a delightful nursing Sister, Rachel, whom we had met on the ship we had taken to Hong Kong in December 1937. We were told that the shower in the bathroom was working until 8p.m. The other four had arrived on an earlier ferry and had managed to freshen up. Thank God it had been a hot day, as we could rinse out our grimy clothes, which would dry rapidly. While we were sluicing off the unpleasantness of the journey, Rachel rustled up a couple of mugs of tea and some hot rice gruel. There was not much furniture in the room: camp beds for all but two of us and luckily one for Mother. The blocks and rooms around us were filling up. Having summed each other up, we were thankfully sure we could get along. Our room had a small balcony overlooking the beautiful Tytam Bay. A washing line had already been strung, and was in use. Tomorrow there would be so much to do and find out. We had an electric light which we didn't get much time to appreciate, as soon after we had got ourselves more or less organised it was lights out!

The choice of Stanley Peninsula was perfect for an internment camp. It could be completely isolated from the rest of the Island, but transport and communications were normal. The area was originally occupied by the prison staff. There was also St Stephens College, with boarding quarters for the boys and bungalows for the masters and their families. The rest was taken up with warders' married quarters, single quarters, and the Indian warders' quarters, a club house for prison officers, hospital and cemetery. We had a glorious view south, east and west, of the sea, beaches, bays and islands. Our perimeter stopped at the junction where the main road from the island of Hong Kong branched. To the right the road ran along the coast up to the tip of the peninsula which had been the Stanley Garrison, now housing a Japanese garrison. To the left it cut through the camp, stopping at Stanley jail, a dead end. Outside our boundary at the start of the road were the quarters for the guards and the dreaded Gendarmerie, equivalent to Nazi-Gestapo. The main village was on the west side of the peninsula, and the fishing fleet's anchorage the bay on the east, while to the north were the wooded hills between us and the rest of Hong Kong island.

Up the hill to the left of the main road were the houses and gardens of the Commissioner of Prisons and his deputy. On the same hill St Stephens College had their quarters and bungalows. On the left of the road, at a lower level, were the warders' quarters, and the club house. A branch road led up to their buildings. The hospital was set aside on yet a lower level, directly overlooking Tytam Bay. To the right of the forbidding jail was a large field with tool sheds, used by the prisoners who grew their own vegetables. A cemented path ran the length of the west wall of the jail to a lovely secluded beach known as Tweed Bay, and formerly almost exclusively for the use of the Governor of Hong Kong and his guests.

The jail walls were at least forty feet high, with the lookout towers at each corner. In front was a large parade ground, and a driveway up to the houses on the hill. There was a road leading to the hospital off the left of the parade ground, which was out of bounds for all internees. The cemetery was on the far west and slightly below the hill housing the bungalows.

On the right of the coast road, as it branched off to the garrison, was a large playing field, with several small residences for the post office and local police station. For the first few weeks, for some unaccountable reason, we were allowed to use this field for exercise, under armed guards. However, this was abruptly forbidden after the escapes.

Our Commander-in-Chief and Governor had elected to be taken as a POW. He was, after all, a soldier first. His deputy was to act on behalf of the internees. He was to choose a committee from the many able men interned, and liaise with the Japanese Camp Commandant.

The four main blocks for housing in our area were known as the 'Married quarters', the 'Indian quarters', the 'American quarters' and the 'Dutch quarters'.

This last block housed the Dutch community and the few Belgians who were interned with the British. By the second week in February the bulk of the internees were in camp. There were roughly 2,800 people, including about 300 Americans and 60 plus Dutch and Belgians. Amongst the British were a small number of Canadians. There was still a contingent of nurses in Kowloon.

The Japanese Commandant and his staff naturally installed themselves in the two houses up the hill. The camp office was in the married quarters where our President was based.

During the first weeks we were busy taking stock of our encampment. Kitchens had been set up in convenient sectors of the camp. Changes, too, were taking place in the original allocation of accommodation, people rearranging their rooms, families who had been separated being billeted together. Most of the bungalows had been resourcefully grabbed by the first arrivals, either for their companies, families or friends. Priorities were naturally given to the administrative staff, kitchen staff, and hospital staff who could not be accommodated in the hospital building.

The rest of us sorted ourselves out as best we could. Our group elected to stay where we were, except

Rachel who left us to join the other nursing staff.

Having got our bearings, the next thing was to search out friends and get our duty rosters organised. The shaking down process was amazingly cheerful despite the usual crop of Cassandras! The Peak residents, who had mostly come by road, managed to make arrangements for various trunks and suitcases to be delivered. Many loyal Chinese came to the main gate with parcels of food and toiletries which, in those early days of confusion, were allowed.

The vital essential services for the camp were the first priorities. With water rationing, teams were formed to cope with the indoor sanitary disposal. With almost everyone having the trots, it was vital to keep the toilets emptied, a most offensive task.

There were wood cutters, ration collection, and volunteers for many dreary jobs to be recruited. Most of the younger women like myself, were put to vegetable cleaning and cutting, and keeping the rooms and corridors within our own premises free of dirt. Other duties would be meted out when the final rosters were drawn up. Our greatest asset was in having professionals in almost every walk of life. Secret radio communications were set up. Schools were started. An entertainment committee began to plan their programmes. Men from the Public Works Department were available for any building problems. There were the doctors and nurses from the Health Service, carpenters, tailors, and of course our padres, as well as the Jesuit fathers, all of whom set up regular services and the police force who inspired a sense of security.

The lifeline of the camp was, naturally, made up by the cooks and their kitchen staff. The meagre rations would not stretch to more than two inadequate meals per day, one at 11a.m. and the last at 5p.m.

The culinary imagination of the unvaried menus were masterpieces! The highlights were: 'navy blue stew with rice' (the taro vegetable being blue when cooked); 'eyeball and arsehole soup with rice' (fish heads and tails boiled); 'gristle and greens with rice' and 'seaweed delicacies with rice'.

On special occasions the rice would be ground into flour for an evening meal treat, pasties filled with whatever greens had been provided, well flavoured, when possible, with garlic.

In the very early days there were times when the ration lorries did not arrive. Parties of our men were detailed by the Japanese to collect broken sacks of rice from the government food godowns a short distance from our boundary. These godowns had at sometime been bombed by the Japanese, and the rice spilling over the floor was liberally mixed with broken glass. The myth that ground glass could be used as a murder weapon was exploded. There was no way of separating the glass from the rice, except for the obvious pieces, so we just chomped it up. If a sliver of window pane happened to be in a mouthful you simply picked, or spat it out!

The black market, christened 'the Blacks', began to flourish. The organisation was similar to the bowling game of ten pins. The top brass was the King Pin. His deputy recruited suitable candidates in the various areas to handle the supplies, essentially food and cigarettes. There was still quite a bit of currency and jewellery amongst the internees. More profitable, large companies both local and international, whose IOUs could help augment the rations for themselves and any of their staff who also happened to be in camp. This illegal trading was a real necessity as long as there were hungry and sick customers, for there was no alternative way of getting any extras.

It was acknowledged that the manual workers would have to get supplementary rations. Also that supplies of milk, fruit, sugar, if and when delivered, would be given first priority for the hospital, the children and the older people, in that order. Salt would be provided for the kitchens and a small tea ration given directly to the internees. These brews were so often watered down that the panacea for all ailments became known as 'gnat's pee'.

Under the administration as set up on our arrival, the Stanley village traders were allowed to offer their wares for sale at the main gate, so that groups of us would pool sufficient dollars together to buy various additions for the diet: Chinese buns, eggs, tins of condensed milk, and the delicious Chinese sugar slabs, wong tong. This didn't last very long before the Blacks got a corner on the market, and the modest purchases of small syndicates came to a sorrowful end! It did mean, though, that we had been able to lay by a modest stock of the unperishables.

The kitchens managed to bake limited quantities of bread, in the beginning, and blocks took it in turns for their day in the bread queue. Alas, the stock of flour finally ran out and was not replenished. Mother, who enjoyed her slice with a scraping of condensed milk on it, dismissed the vanished luxury as hardly worth eating without thick butter and a dollop of black cherry jam!

A relatively cheap, and highly prized buy for the room was a large bottle of mango chutney. A smear added to one of the dull day's menu helped to revive the taste buds.

One of the least favourite vegetables on the cleaning and cutting rosters was taro. It spat out a stinking shower of liquid which swelled and blistered the hands. Being told that under running water this didn't happen was a big help, as at that time there was no running water. The end result for the day's meals was glutinous ladles of navy blue gunge!

Bog-bailing was the most degrading of all our duties, but a vital necessity for the health of the camp. It meant literally bailing out the toilets, and disposing of the contents where directed by the sanitary department. Fortunately, when the public services had been restored the duty roster was required less frequently!

The problems of organisation were handled by the experts. Supplies were needed for the hospital, and the schools, repairing damages to the buildings which suffered during the battle on the Stanley Peninsula. Blankets, camp beds, eating utensils, all the hundreds of necessary things normally accepted for everyday life.

One of the most difficult physical aspects causing anguish amongst the women was the wretched monthly cycle. There were no sanitary towels to be begged, borrowed, or stolen. The hospital was desperately in need of material for dressings. None of us, if we had any, had come to camp with a sufficient supply of this necessity; the only substitution was a coarse brown paper that had been issued as toilet paper. It proved to be almost more depressing mentally than physically. However, Mother Nature quite rapidly took care of this female bodily function, which for the majority of the younger women became a closed circuit. The side effect was most unsightly, We blew up like the proverbial gas balloons. Our puffy faces and bloated limbs became the butt of suggestions that we must be raiding the kitchen stores, which caused more anguish and embarrassment, until word got round that this was a readjustment problem too!

A strict routine had not yet been established. The first Camp Commandant appointed by the Japanese was a Chinese gentleman. The interpreter was a Japanese who was both fluent in Chinese and English, and indeed known as a local businessman. Between them they wisely allowed our own authorities to do the sorting out, giving as much help as they could to relieve the most pressing situations. When the Japanese had the Chinese population under control, and Hong Kong and mainland functioning, then, and only then, would they consider setting up their own administration over the camp.

In view of the impending take-over of the camp by the Japanese, a prominent Englishman, a professor of Japanese culture, and fluent in the language, was asked to give a series of lectures to try and explain their attitude towards the vanquished. They had never experienced the surrender of fighting men. Their code was that you fought to the death, on the field of battle, on the seas and in the air. POWs were the lowest form of scum, only fit to do subservient tasks and be humiliated. The tremendous number of women, children and male civilians to be coped with was a daunting proposition. The camp guards were, for the most part, young men trained on the barrack squares in their homeland and brainwashed as to their invincibility. Few if any had ever seen a white face. Theirs was a bewildering duty. Arrogance was tinctured with a certain amount of apprehension. The older members in their ranks, more experienced, helped bolster the certainty that they were the superior race. As such the Imperial Emperor's forces would be victorious in their aim to establish the Greater East Asia Co-Prosperity Sphere. Their only goal was their duty to their Emperor-God, Country and Family. To achieve this they would gladly die.

# 3

---

During those early weeks of confusion plans were
being laid to arrange escapes. As yet no roll-calls had
been instituted, so that there was a good chance of
not being discovered missing for perhaps a couple of
days. Any escape would have to be with the co-
operation of Chinese on the outside. No white faces,
without the knowledge of at least Chinese, could
possibly find their way alone to any escape route.

Obviously the easiest route was by small sampan
through the fishing fleet. The quickest route to the
beach was from the 'club' quarters across the main
road nearest the cemetery. The club was already
occupied by several men who had taken over the
upper floor. They were mostly journalists. Jo Alsop,
a famous American was the leader. Rumours, of
course, were clogging the so-called news, every day.
Chinese from outside the camp were still able to get
in to visit their former bosses, friends and the odd
relative. As discipline was incredibly muddled and
slack, the men planning their escape were able to
have long sessions with their Chinese helpers. Almost
anyone you talked to was breathing secrets of great
escapes being organised – large, small, men only.
Several canny women were included in the 'big plans'.
There was in fact one woman, Gwen Drew, who made

her escape on the same night as the Alsop group.

The fateful morning arrived. Word travelled round like wildfire that there had been no less than two escapes the night before, discovered quite by chance by the guards. It so happened that neither party had the remotest idea that there was a second escape planned to take place on the same night; it was coincidental. This was attributed to the fact that the escapes were blown so quickly.

All internees were immediately confined to their quarters. The maniacal fury of the Commandant and the guards spread through each isolated and heavily guarded area.

Only those billeted nearest the escapees could possibly know who they were. They were being mercilessly interrogated by the Gendarmerie. Rumours of a complete get away, of recapture, of who they were, kept us on tenterhooks.

By dusk there was a fearsome lull over the whole camp. No lights were allowed, no meals. The whisper was universal, there had been no recapture. Hardly daring to believe, we milled about, celebrating in stale cold tea to quiet our rumbling tummies.

That they had made good their escapes was indeed true. Both plans had been brilliantly executed, aided by loyal and gallant Chinese friends. Their stories have long since been recorded. This dramatic event was a tremendous morale booster. We less adventurous souls went back to our dreams of repatriation.

Security was at once stepped up. Extra armed guards were produced. There appeared to be little chance of any further illegal exits from the camp. The Gendarmerie had not been very gentle with the escapees' neighbours. They were fortunate that they had at least been thrown back into camp, where they were taken to hospital for treatment to their vicious wounds.

At the same time we had heard news of several successful escapes by our POWs in Shamshuipo camp in Kowloon. Later we learned the officers had been moved to a new camp in Argyle Street – where escape was considered impossible. We were cocooned in a state of euphoria, tinged with fear.

For most of the internees the possibility that women and children would be repatriated was a gleam of hope on the horizon. But for those of us with husbands, fathers or sons in the POW camps, that gleam was dulled by the fact of leaving them even further away. Very little news had reached us from the Kowloon camps, except a heart-chilling message that a diphtheria epidemic was claiming many lives. Although no official communication had as yet been arranged between the camps, the fact that they were only a few miles apart, as the old crow flies, gave us some comfort. There were still ways of conveying important items of news, such as the several escapes already made, which had been successful.

Life began to take on a semblance of normalcy. The club house being in easy access to most areas of the camp, was used for the kindergarten, lectures, and the library. Permission had been given for the library from the American Club in town to be transferred to camp. The bar in the club was the obvious setting: a high solid counter, behind which were the three-sided rows of shelves for the books, and sufficient room for two people to work. As I had some experience as a librarian in the American Club, the committee suggested Joyce and myself be in charge.

We laboriously evolved a system of loaning out the books on a strict time and honour basis. It was arranged to open alternate mornings and afternoons so as not to clash heavily with the various daily chores. These sessions soon became the focal point for meeting up with friends. The library then developed into a 'post office' where notes could be left for collection. Many camp rumours were passed around this way, not all authentic.

The aggravation we faced during the opening weeks was that books were being defiled. Those books containing dirty or blasphemous words were heavily blacked out! After some pretty canny detective work we were able to pin down a section of the community, who by elimination, had to be the culprits. A lot of tact was required to filter through to them that they were rumbled, that by refraining from borrowing this offensive material, the majority of readers, who had no such scruples, could enjoy the privileges of the library!

The men, of course, dubbed the library the pub. They developed a language of their own, asking for the third bottle of scotch or gin from the left or right of whatever shelf, or whatever position the particular book they wanted happened to occupy. We got very professional at reaching for the right one as time went on! This was an amusing diversion, as it usually brought forth memories of happy 'bashes' followed by formidable hangovers!

Reference books, adventure stories and cookery books were most in demand, with Shakespeare and the Bible, both Old and New Testaments, running a close second!

We soon realised that we could only open the library four days a week. Joyce worked in a confidential capacity with the administrative office, as well as having her own chores to do. Her mother, who was with her in camp, was not at all well, so that during those first long weeks she was in and out of the hospital very often. This was an extra burden for Joyce. It was sad that our mothers, who had known each other for many years, were hardly ever in agreement. They were both Irish!

Library duty was one of the more fun details on our roster. Being the local meeting place, we gradually re-met friends we had not seen since the beginning of the war, and were able to catch up on their experiences. In fact, Joyce did suggest to one of the girls who was very friendly with the Blacks' King Pin, that he should open a morning coffee bar and an afternoon 'Ye Olde Shoppe' tea. The American community had already got permission to have a well-known caterer provide them with a Sunday brunch. The enticing smells wafting across camp during these sessions were not popular with the non-participants! However, with strong rumours that the Americans were soon to be repatriated, this civilised habit was soon to end.

Early in March we were told that the library wold have to close down until further notice. We were stunned. Finally it was officially announced that the Japanese authorities had agreed, after some diplomatic pressure, to open a canteen in the club premises. The canteen would be stocked for a week. Each day members of the various sections of camp would be allowed to buy a limited amount of supplies for their group.

This was splendid news. Even for those of us with small amounts of cash, the idea of browsing around a mini-Harrods, as we imagined it would be, was exciting enough!

In due course the area notice boards gave the day,

times and rules for participation. Only those people recruited to serve in the canteen were allowed in the club house, or in the vicinity, which was heavily guarded as the supplies arrived.

Everyone rushed around wildly, trying to figure out the procedure, which of course included queues. Orders and positions in which these queues were to be formed were first on the list. Our room was in chaos; we were 'Married quarters' Block 4, room 14. Having read, and re-read the notice board, we were still not any the wiser as to how to organise ourselves. Mother finally worked out the master plan!

'All these regulations are too confusing. Forget them. One of you younger ones will join the first available queue, or better still, start one, people are bound to join up behind you! We will make out our lists tonight, and hand over our money. You'll see, it will all work out splendidly.'

By special permission we were allowed to leave our quarters to join the block queues at daybreak the following morning. It was decided that I would take the first shift as my roster for the day included vegetable cutting when the ration trucks came in. There were three of us to do the queueing, leaving the two mums to fortify us with a brew when we were wilting.

Compiling our list was hilarious. There was no paper to waste on frivolous suggestions. However, we were allowed to voice our first choice for a laugh. Mother opted for a blue hair rinse – she was sick of looking like an 'African Grey'! Nan longed for a pair of roller skates to take the boredom out of endless treks. There were a few outrageous requests before we got down to the serious business of necessary items to be purchased, with the money we had in the communal kitty to splurge on this fabulous opportunity! So with tummies aching with laughter, for a change, we finally agreed on a large bottle of real shampoo to be equally shared. Depending on how far we could stretch our budget, and availability in the canteen, spending importance naturally focused on FOOD. Nan's boyfriend, who worked in the hospital, had mysteriously produced a small, rather battered cardboad carton rescued from the stores department, no doubt; and we were in business!

At the crack of sparrow-fart, gulping down the remains of a mug of cold tea Mother had saved from the last brew, I scurried down the stairs to join the nearest forming queue – I had no intention of starting one! In the early morning light, figures could be seen hurrying to take up their positions in what was already a formidably lengthy line all the way past our blocks. Murder, grab a place. Having found the tail of the queue, I lowered myself on to my hunkers to prepare for the long wait.

After the early morning chill the sun was very comforting, and we took stock of our position. Everywhere one looked there were streams of people, excitedly chattering, bored guards, and home-made camp stools being loaned up and down the lines. Someone behind me shoved a seat under my rear end. The sun was getting to the sizzling stage. I began to nod off, a rather tricky operation on a camp stool, but possible!

My siesta was suddenly interrupted by a slight shake of my right arm. Discovering a gap in front of me, I snapped back to reality. Behind me was a would-be customer who said cheerfully through toothless gums, 'You'd better move on, luv, or you'll miss the bus.' How right he was; the figure in front was at least four feet away. Progress! Passing the stool to my new-found friend we started chatting.

He told me that he had lost his 'dencheurs' in a Wanchai bar during the hostilities. He was having a nice cold beer when there was a Christ-Almighty crash, right beside him, well, not exactly that close, but bloody near, see. He took out his precious teeth 'because they were clacking with fright', and put them, he thought, in a pocket. As the debris hurtled around, the customers were diving under tables, including his girl. That's how he lost his valuable 'piece of furniture'. 'Never mind, luv.' His lips disappeared in a grin. 'I'm hoping that ole Toothy, when we get one, will tart me up with a new pair of snappers that I can sink into them joosy steaks our hosts are planning to provide!'

Poor Buttsy, as he became known to us, finally ran out of butts. 'On account of when the Blacks upped the price of fags, most of the smokers saved their butts until they had collected enough to re-roll them,' would have been his response. He never did get his 'snappers', nor 'his joosy steaks'. He was one of the earliest customers for the cemetery.

Nan came with a welcome mug. Buttsy declined sharing it; he was wanting a nice cold beer! There was really no need for Nan to take over; we were moving quite steadily, and Buttsy had a lot more interesting yarns to spin me! I did, however, borrow Nan's cloth hat.

After what seemed a million light years, a clutch of six of us made the canteen. The disappointment was suicidal. We shuffled amongst empty boxes, surrounded by shelves holding nothing but boot polish and shoelaces! How could I possibly face my roommates, eagerly awaiting some small luxury? Seething with rage and frustration we filed out with our tails between our legs to an angry crowd. They had been warned that there was nothing left to be bought, but were still standing around hopefully. I was determined to find out why we had been shepherded into this wilderness of useless stock.

Perhaps tomorrow, after the re-stocking, Nan would be lucky. That evening the notice board clearly gave the message – NO FURTHER CANTEENS!

If the remaining disappointed clients had not been so weary and disillusioned, there would have been a riot.

Word was circulated that owing to the disruption caused in camp routine, it had been decided etc., etc. That night I searched out a friend who had been one of the cashiers in the canteen. He explained that the night before a number of the higher echelon had been allowed in for first choice, albeit a very limited one. Stocks were difficult to get from the city, prices were soaring, and undoubtedly the Blacks had cornered the market. He was just as bitter as the rest of us. 'Christ,' he said, 'don't you realise this is an internment camp, not a picnic?'

'Too true, old luv,' Buttsy would have remarked.

At least the canteen cock-up would be grist to our increasing load of grumbles, which would be thoroughly aired at the reopening of the library. That was a day to look forward to, a plethora of new rumours and surely a list of a few unfamiliar adjectives.

Andrew was directly involved with the camp committee, a full-time job, especially in those early days beset with problems. He still found time to visit Mother and me. He was showing the strain of the last few months of unavoidable responsibility. The tall

51

thin figure was thinner, and slightly stooped. His brown hair and moustache were liberally streaked with grey, but his mood was always cheerful.

The most dangerous situation developing was the rumoured crop of 'illegal' radios. These were bound to jeopardise the radio set up under the strictest security and secrecy, with the blessing of the camp president and committee.

By word of mouth, suspected radio operators were warned that they were endangering the 'official' radio, and the lives of those operating the instrument, but the rumours persisted that word was filtering through to the Japanese that there were several radios throughout the camp.

It was obviously foolhardy for the professionals to contact the office regularly with their reports. Brief items could be passed on by word of mouth. This method could only be used with the co-operation of personal friends of the radio operators. So it was that on one of Andrew's visits, he casually suggested that he and I take a walk 'via Siberia'. This was the most popular form of evening's exercise, encircling the camp's barbed wire perimeter. During the stroll Andrew explained the difficulty, adding that as Peter, who recruited couriers and was a close friend of my family, and I were often seen together would I be willing to act as courier. Others with friends in similar circles would be acting in the same capacity. Naturally this conversation, whether I agreed to the proposition or not, was to be entirely forgotten because of the implications. Poor Andrew, he had been given an awesome task to entrust me with, and he looked quite sick with fear when the answer was 'of course'. From now on, Peter and I would make our own arrangements.

The importance attached to any word of what was happening beyond our confines was our life-blood. Although most of the early reports were not very encouraging, the ritual of exchanging tidbits collected during the day, never varied. Each evening, after curfew, there were huddles of us in the corridors, and on the landings, avidly awaiting the choicest rumour from 'a reliable' source! As the messages Peter gave me to relay to the office were very infrequent, and not for re-broadcasting, my main contact was Fred.

A big wheel in one of the colony's leading hotels to which he had transferred from Shanghai in 1937, he had a vast network of informers. He was a well-built, witty Englishman, a great golfing and sailing companion of my father. Chantal, his French wife, was small, dark and very chic. Fred's news 'bulletin', if it arrived, did not do so until well after curfew. Most nights it was fairly easy to nip across to their block which was over the road, and therefore out of bounds after curfew. Fred had been assigned an amah's room which could only hold two people without being 'overcrowded'. Chantal would usually have a hot brew for me, a terrific treat, while Fred would give me pieces of information to take back. A harbinger of cheerful outside-world items only, he wisely kept any bits of gloom between himself and possibly Chantal.

On this particular night Fred met me inside the block entrance, to say Chantal was not very well and was trying to sleep; also that he had nothing to report. I was a bit surprised as during the day there had been distant sounds of heavy gunfire, which convinced us that there must be some exciting reports. Disappointed, I waited for the guard to tramp past. As we stood quietly in the shadow of the building a figure

53

joined us, and planting himself next to me, whispered 'what's the news tonight?'

There was a painful jab in my ribs from Fred, who hissed at me 'SCOOT'. The road was clear, my reaction speedy; the roar 'come back' from behind had a decidedly Japanese accent.

The shout had aroused the attention of one of the guards, who must have been lurking in a nearby doorway for a quick smoke. He took up the chase. There was no point in diving into my own quarter, I would be cornered. My room-mates would not appreciate me arriving with an irate guard hot on my heels! So having got plenty of steam up, kept going round and between the buildings. Fortunately, I was far more familiar with the layout than the guard; neither was I hampered by rifle and bayonet!

By this time people in the blocks were disturbed at the clatter he was making. Cries of 'What's the trouble?' echoed round the courtyard. Very breathless, I made the dark haven of a back entrance. Shooting in and up the stairway to the first floor, I stood panting back against the wall! After an eternity a voice said quietly, 'All's well, off to your room.'

Fortunately for me, in those early days it was difficult to impose reprisals for infringements of minor rules. That slackness changed immediately the Japanese commandant was posted to take control of the camp.

Fred contacted me the following morning. He had waited, watching, until the guard had finally appeared alone. Our companion of the night before turned out to be one of the Japanese interpreters, who was in fact visiting his pre-war employee living in the same quarters as Fred! After an amiable chat it was agreed to forget the 'incident'. The interpreter then had a few words with the guard, back in his box, and returned to resume his friendly visit. He and Fred had often exchanged greetings until the military takeover, when the interpreter was relieved of his duties. 'Pity, useful chap on occasions, wants his job back after the war!' Fred didn't expand on his usefulness, but it could have been contacts.

The persistent rumour that a Japanese commandant, with his personal staff, would relieve the present band of merry men directing operations, became a fact. Our Camp President, with his committee, were summoned Up-The-Hill to be formally briefed. When the President was finally allowed to speak, he tried tactfully to explain that though morale was fairly high in the circumstances, overcrowding and lack of sufficient rations and medical supplies, could lead to an explosive condition. The disdainful reply was that the issue of low rations would make any effort at violence impossible, and that if the camp authorities could not cope with a rebellion, he could, and would. Round one to his side.

He was Colonel Tanaka, and his immediate order was that there would be a full roll call-the following morning, starting with the married quarters. In his opinion, discipline was slack and the internees needed a firmer hand, which he intended to apply.

We were delighted to be the first on call. Get the frills over with so that we could get back to business. Nonetheless there was a nervous unease as to how much firmer a hand the new broom would apply.

The morning started off on a gloomy note, hot, steamy with the threat of rain and thunderstorms. On the bright side the knowledge gained from experience was that our hosts did not enjoy lingering in the wet either, so there was a chance that our spell on parade would be as brief as possible.

As we lined up in blocks, behind the President and committee, a warm damp drizzle gave the pessimists a chance to predict a long wet wait. The guards were fanning out along the route our new Commandant would take to reach us for the countdown. A table from the office was placed in front of the untidy and already restless ranks. Thus we would all be able to see the august Colonel. Likewise no lowly internee would be able to look down on the representative of His Imperial Majesty, the Emperor.

Still no sign of any activity Up-The-Hill, which we could see from the parade ground. The drizzle was drifting off towards the sea. Several of the younger kids started playing catch between the columns, ignoring the fretful calls from parents. The older people, with their stools, began to lower themselves for a short sit. Most of the rest of us fidgeted about, passing the odd snide remark to each other. One wag called out for a tea break, which set off a volley of suggestions as to how he could go about it! Through a sudden divide in the clouds the sun came out, fiercely hot, shrouding us in a sauna bath, the steam from our damp bodies fogging the view.

There was a series of bellows from the distance. The guards snapped sharply into position, their bayonets afire with sunbeams. Our President raised his arms, a plea for order. We shuffled back into some form of tidy rows, with the help of a bit of shoving from the line behind, or a neighbour. Stools were folded, the kids rounded up, and returned to their places. In the unnatural quiet that seemed to hang like a spider's thread, the steady beat of horses' hooves came drumming up the road between the line of guards.

As if rehearsed, you could hear the collective catch of breath. Three magnificent chestnut mounts walked proudly into view. The Colonel in full panoply, besporting an absurdly long sword, followed behind by two of his officers.

In the awful silence, a voice from our ranks could be heard quite clearly. 'Just like the bloody Victory Parade.'

The spell was broken. Loud coughs, a few tentative nervous giggles, and amid much hissing and sucking of teeth amongst the guards the Colonel mounted the rostrum, his horse being held by one of the officers and the second officer still astride his animal, on the Colonel's left.

Taking our cue from the committee, we went through the bowing ceremony. The harangue started with a brief bark from the Colonel. The officer on his left, obviously the interpreter, carefully relayed the message. Although all eyes were riveted on our new commandant, no one was really listening. Our thoughts wandered to that longed-for refreshing mug of tea, or perhaps the last time we had been to the races.

There was another longer bark from the Colonel, as the officer prepared himself to deliver the text. An excited squeal from one of the children sliced across the crowd: 'Mummy, mummy, LOOK, he's doing a PO-PO.'

The horse gave a whinny. One great guffaw started a daisy chain of hysterical laughter, it got louder and more out of hand. Whilst we were collapsing on the ground, or hugging each other for support, trying desperately to control ourselves, a bunch of kids, sensing the slack in the tension, stormed round the offending 'PO-PO' to stare in wonder at this enormous feat.

Exhausted, the laughter sputtered out. Apoplectic guards roughly hauled us into line, indulging in an orgy of face-slapping. Only the committee, still standing forlornly in their place, had witnessed the departure of the Colonel and his entourage. In his place on the desk, stood the small figure of our original interpreter, who announced that the punishment for insulting His Imperial Majesty, as ordered by our Commandant, was that we would remain on parade until he saw fit to dismiss us.

The old boy behind Mother settled back on his stool: 'Silly lot of sods!' he grunted, rubbing his aching back, 'no sense of humour.'

'Well,' replied Mother, wrapping the whole Japanese nation in one sentence. 'What do you expect from a pig but a grunt!'

So it was that the pessimists' prediction of a long wait proved right; in fact it was an ordeal. However, later in the afternoon the threatened thunderstorm broke. Not waiting for the 'dismiss' signal, we all belted for the shelter of our quarters. This Act of God had not been included in the original punishment. Thus 'faces' were saved!

Under the new regime each area was to elect a spokesman, known as the Blockhead, to be a combination of Nannie, arbitrator and father confessor. Phil, an affable bachelor, was persuaded by us to take on this unenviable duty for Block 14.

From the very beginning the camp had been plagued by patrols of guards, sometimes accompanied by an officer, making sneaky late night spot checks. On occasions they would be unpleasantly drunk and growling for a woman. Lurching into various rooms, shining a powerful spotlight unsteadily round the once sleeping figures and making obscene signs, they enjoyed prodding us with their rifle stocks to get up and bow them off the premises.

Our men devised a system of a pair of lookouts who could give a warning to the shadows lurking in the corridors, on the landings, anywhere it was possible to find a bit of privacy, a chance to scurry back to their burrows. For the late night watches the men had drawn up their roster with volunteers from the women to stand in with the chap in Jap-spotting. Duty meant we only had one night, or at the most two, a week to do our turn.

Phil very wisely did not try to reorganise the system. It was a bit haphazard, but seemed to work out for the most part. He did cheer us up by telling us that the President was going to appeal to the Colonel, for the sake of the children in particular, for fewer nightly disturbances. In the meantime, when there was no spot check, those quiet hours with a pleasant companion to talk over the news and events of the day, and the possible future, helped one to accept the completely alien existence.

Rick was one of my favourite lookout partners. Tall, broad-shouldered, with solemn brown eyes and a wide smile, he had a cynical wit, and liked taking the steam out of anyone the least bit pompous. Janie, his strikingly lovely wife, was recovering from a back injury when they came into camp, so was unable to share in the lookout duties. As their billet was across the corridor we met early on, and became good friends. Janie had been hoarding a packet of prunes, so when it was my turn to be his second, he would arrive with a prune each. For as long as they lasted I used to keep the stones to suck like a boiled sweet, palming off the new one for Mother! Although the

59

spot checks continued despite the President's appeal, an officer was always present. This precaution helped keep the guards under control and the periodic disturbances were treated as just another indignity, hopefully without the fear of molestation.

Amongst the bungalows they were not so fortunate. Being used to fraternising within their area, they grew careless. There were several very nasty beatings-up, if one of the men were caught slipping home, having spent an after curfew session with his girl-friend out of bounds.

One distressing, near fatal beating involved a young teenager. Robert was an overgrown, wild thirteen-year-old. His mother had two younger sons to cope with and found Robert quite unmanageable. This particular night he had not returned at curfew. As this had happened before when he was visiting chums in the same building, his mother shrugged it off. Robert, however, was visiting farther afield and, skulking back in the shadows, he ran straight into a patrol. As he was lunged at by one of the guards he fought like a maniac to go free. Three of the Japanese set upon him, beating him senseless. The terrible screams and Japanese shouts brought people out of their quarters. The eventual realisation that he was only a youngster increased their fury. The other internees who tried to stop the furious attack were also victims of their rifle butts.

Attracted by the clamour and the sound of a rifle shot, the duty officer at nearby headquarters appeared on the scene with reinforcements. A powerful torch pinpointed the fracas. After a brief report from the guards he dismissed them. Then, ordering the boy to be lifted on to a blanket which the two injured internees were told to carry like a hammock, he screamed 'HOSPITAL'. They painfully picked their way down the slope with two relief guards behind. Robert's mother followed the litter, sobbing forlornly. The angry knots of people were dispersed. The officer returned to headquarters without a backward glance.

The following day this 'incident' was released to the camp by the Commandant as a warning of what to expect for our contempt of his orders.

The only other 'incident' took place much later and information about it was only released by the internees involved. There was an old rice wine distillery just outside the camp perimeter. Sometimes a few bottles of this potent brew were smuggled in. Four of our chaps were having a quiet tipple on their back steps, technically not out of bounds. The patrol spotted them, but before any alarm was raised, one of the lads, who had picked up quite a bit of Japanese, suggested they sample the wine and give their opinion of its potency. The two guards, utterly bored by their dreary duty, and flattered no doubt at being addressed in their own language, proceeded to do a thorough job of sampling. The quiet tipple seemed to be developing into a party, which could be dangerous. So when the guards were feeling no pain, and started to get singing drunk, the boys carefully steered them down towards the barbed wire boundary across the beach of the Indian quarters, leaving them to find their way home from their drunken orgy!

Prudently, in the likely case of a search being made in their area the next morning, they heaved the empties, which they filled with sand, as far as possible into the heavy scrub around the rocks. Reluctantly, they did the same with their last precious full bottle.

There were no repercussions.

Apart from night lookouts, volunteers were needed as extra hands in all camp activities. The hospital, situated in its own compound, away from the main area of the camp but within the perimeter, was first priority. There was always a waiting list for a bed. Patients with minor ailments, which still required medical attention, were fitted in like tinned sardines, on makeshift mattresses, wherever there was an empty floor space.

Raw recruits were welcome to help on night duty. This was a comparatively quiet period. There was always at least one nursing sister in charge who could be referred to if one got in a panic. My first attempt as Florence Nightingale was in the men's ward. The less serious cases were talking softly, sharing a drag-on-a-fag, or peering over some sheet of reading matter under the one dim peanut oil lamp allowed in each ward. Most of them were dozing restlessly.

The view from the promontory on which the hospital was built, was full of happy nostalgia. Tweed Bay Beach, the little magic island set darkly in the faintly glowing sea reaching far out to the horizon, was taking me dreamily back into time. A sudden jolt into the present was a low, but urgent gruff voice: 'Over here Miss, I want a water bottle.'

'Coming up.' I rallied, making for the corridor.

Outside the wards, on trestle tables, were the bare essentials: a few mugs, bottles of drinking water, bedpans, a couple of odd-shaped empty bottles, a small pile of rough squares of paper. Nervously I half filled a mug with drinking water, making my way in the direction from which the voice had come. There was a deliberate hush, followed by an exasperated bellow: 'I don't want to drink it, you silly bitch, I want to PISS in it.'

The rest of the ward broke up. The howls of mirth and succinct remarks brought the sister in charge at the double. Having sorted the problem out she signed me to follow her, whereupon she initiated me into the jargon. At least I had learned my lesson in an understanding atmosphere. Not allowed to forget my embarrassing gaffe, the standard greeting from the men's ward on my arrival was 'Here comes bring-the-bottle-kid!'

One repatriation rumour finally came true. The Americans were going home! Their jubilation was shared by us all. They had been wonderful companions, and had done their load of communal duties cheerfully. The contingent of Jesuit priests from the seminary in the village of Stanley Peninsula contributed zealously to camp activities. Teaching, caring for their flock and attacking every task they were set with good humour and vigor, they would be sadly missed. Mother, who had been a wayward daughter of her religion, found great comfort at being drawn back into the fold.

Having worked with an American company in peace time, the family had many good and close friends amongst them – Jack in particular, who had been my long-suffering and patient boss! A few days after the news that the *Gripsholm* would be carrying them off, Jack told me, breathless with excitement, that the Consul General was sure he could arrange to include me with the repatriates. He had already listed two other British women who had worked for the Consulate. Unfortunately, there was no possible way Mother could also come along. I was staggered at this unbelievable gesture. However unpredictable and churlish, to put it moronically, I simply couldn't accept. Mother and I had no news of Pa, who had been in Singapore when the Pacific war broke, no news of my husband since he had become a POW and I wouldn't entertain leaving Mother; it was unthinkable.

As the momentous day drew closer our American friends shared out their belongings: camp cots, tea, coffee, sugar and biscuits! Most important, blankets, clothing and SOAP. Mel, a Southern charmer, with whom I occasionally joined on sanitary disposal duty, invited Joyce and me to a farewell lunch on the hillside: a sumptuous meal, two whole tins of sardines and a packet of cream crackers followed by a tin of peaches! Mel had thoughtfully kept a portion of each course for our two mothers. Joyce and I gobbled down our sardines, bones included. Mel was quite shocked when we removed the bones he had fussily scraped onto the edge of his chipped plate, to add to our own.

Departure date was finalised and excited lines of repatriates were route-marched down to the beach on which we had landed a lifetime of some six months before. Our messages and addresses of families were safely tucked away in their small bundles. At the very last moment, the Jesuit father figure refused to leave with his compatriots. As long as one member of the Roman Catholic faith remained, he would be there for guidance and comfort.

Whilst the Americans sang their way to the beach, amid cheers and tears, the rest of us had orders to remain in our quarters. When the passengers were boarded, we were allowed back to our daily routines. Some of us managed to hurry over to the cemetery, from where we could see them sail away, with much waving, and our prayers for their safe arrival home.

It was an emotional day for all of us, and for some who had formed deep friendships, very painful. The added perks were a bonus during those days when it was difficult to see any silver linings on the horizon. One terrific lift was the fact that we knew our messages would get through to our families, fortunes of war being on their side. But it was hard to believe only six months had passed since they had joined us in the camp. The *Gripsholm* was under the auspices of the Red Cross, so hopefully she would get through safely to her point where the refugees she was carrying would be transferred to vessels of their own country.

# 4

The day following the exodus there was a grand upheaval. People took up squatters' rights in empty premises. Allocations were made as fairly as possible by the committee, all of which helped reduce the overcrowding in the blocks.

Unexpectedly, the reduction in rations took a couple of days to filter through to Japanese Headquarters catering department. The Blacks got first advantage of the miscalculation. Nevertheless the area cooks grabbed what was left of the booty to hoard as dry rations for a future non-ration day delivery. The perishable goods, such as they were, gave us all an extra dollop of stew in our bowls!

While it lasted, the half tin of coffee Jack had left us, together with a good-sized thermos flask which we used to wheedle the kitchen staff into filling for us, was a weekly treat for the room. Sunday morning, in the break between chores, a half mug of this nectar was indeed a luxury. One Sunday, when the *Gripsholm* was well on her way, I came back for my coffee break to find Mother in tears. Someone had leaked the story of my chance to be included in the American repatriation. When we were finally alone, she explained how upset she was with my ridiculous decision; she would have to carry the burden of the blame, etc. In the end I pointed out that there was still the possibility of our own repatriation. The dreams we had still not abandoned, and how much more fun for us to be together. The subject was tactfully dropped with a couple of bony hugs!

It was a bit dicey to keep up the lie that we, the British, were going to be repatriated. Being in the Services we all knew Churchill's theory that as long as we held on to HK all would end well. It was common knowledge that Chiang Kai Shek wanted the colony desperately — hence the stories that he and his soldiers were on their way to rescue us. Heaven forbid, were our heartfelt cries!

The King Pin of the Blacks was obviously not expecting any immediate repatriation of the British civilians. His agents were kept well stocked with supplies. Pinnell was his name. He was a business man from the Philippines, caught in Hong Kong on a visit. Medium build, mild manner, with a short military style moustache, grey hair and very dark grey eyes. He had teamed up with an Australian widow whose husband had been killed during the battle for the Island. Della had a bouncy nine-year-old daughter who had been born in Japan. Both of them spoke fluent Japanese, and so the King Pin had recruited Della as his interpreter. She was a friendly soul, always ready to do an extra job if needed. Inevitably many of the internees shunned her, but for the most of us she was only using her extra language as a survival kit.

The Japanese were still allowing essential articles to be brought in. Drugs from the government medical stores, blankets, heavy boots for the workers, school equipment and a limited amount of toilet requirements.

Periodically, friends from the outside were able to deliver packages of items they knew would be useful to us. Life was a hazardous struggle for so many of them who were either unable to, or did not wish to, leave for the comparative safety of the Portuguese island of Macau or the mainland. Their steadfastness was a lifeline to cling to.

There were a number of civilians working under the orders of the Japanese, at their posts in the city: senior banking officials, a few members of the utility services, as well as a contingent of nurses, and a senior medical officer. Most of the nurses were members of the VADs, helping to care for the wounded in both military and civil hospitals. Other than messages smuggled in, there was no official news of their welfare. The only personal contact our committee had was with the Government Health Officer, who had been instrumental in persuading the Japanese that Stanley Peninsula was the obvious site for the internment camp. The doctor had also been ordered to assist with the health problems of the local population until relative order had been restored. On his infrequent visits to the camp he was able to give first hand news of the outside. One item of interest he had heard was that a working party of POWs were being used on a coastal patrol to detect mines, and that they may be used on the Peninsula. The chance that someone in the party might be recognised, should their search be around our beach, opposite the Indian quarters, gave a glimmer of hope.

Many days later orders were given that the inhabitants of the Indian quarters must remain in their rooms until told otherwise and that no one was to venture in that area. Sure enough a heavily guarded group was spotted slowing traversing the beach across the thick rolls of barbed wire. However much eyes were strained it was not possible to be sure of a familiar face, but it was noted that every now and then sand would be scuffed through the wire.

Long after the party had left, and we were free to move about our camp chores, a piece of paper wrapped round a pebble was given to Joyce. It was a brief but heartwarming scrawl that her brother and my husband were OK. Other similar messages were found, and for us lucky ones it was a joyous day.

At one point a very skinny young lad tried to crawl under the wire near the thick bushes at the side of the beach. The tenants of the Indian quarters, right on the beach, heard a couple of shots, but said there did not seem to be anyone wounded, so it was probably a nervous guard letting off a warning shot or two. It was great to know that many messages got to their destination.

The tempo in camp was adjusting. The entertainment committee was in full swing, planning plays, concerts and revues. Individual talents were emerging. Foraging parties managed to crawl through the wire to collect whatever was available from their village contacts. The 'illegal' radio operators were still able to get their bulletins.

One hot August evening Andrew suggested a stroll via Siberia. He looked cheerful but was definitely edgy, and in a hurry to get what he had to say over with. There was a leak in the radio security; no further bulletins were to be issued for the time being. We message carriers must have absolutely no contact with any of the operators. Word was to be spread that no one must be heard to solicit news. There was a real threat of exposure of the professional source, particularly as additional amateurs were in the business.

This was indeed a bitter pill; an informer in the camp was unthinkable.

The following week Andrew's warning was confirmed. At Monday morning's roll-call we were told to remain on parade. A loud groan greeted the announcement. The delay would be a short one. The dreaded Gendarmerie would be making a general search of certain quarters. The familiar knot started in my tummy. One could only pray, that with their strong suspicions, the operators would have had time to dismantle the equipment and have it safely stowed away, or even destroyed.

As Andrew had predicted, there was an informer in the camp, for there was no pretence at a relentless search. The Gendarmerie patrol marched straight to the quarters where Peter and his two operators were billeted. The three men were immediately arrested for having incriminating evidence pointing to radio communications outside the camp. There was no violence from the guard. The three men were roped one behind the other. In a terrifying pall of silence they were marched by the patrol down the road to the Gendarmerie Headquarters outside the main gate into camp. No attempt was made to search any other area, and with a matter-of-fact 'Dismiss' it was all over.

The majority of internees had no idea what it was all about and dispersed, completely stunned by the whole operation. As we went to our alloted duties speculation became rife. The rest of the day passed, the curiosity fading. Andrew came to me that evening, quietly telling me Tanaka had hinted at further reprisals should the President be unable to enforce the Japanese rules on the people. The three men would be given a fair trial, but in the circumstances he foresaw that the death sentence would be pronounced.

'Christ,' said the usually soft spoken Andrew, 'we'll get the bastard who grassed, if it takes forever.'

The next morning, feeling sick and numb, I went up to the cemetery, normally deserted during the early part of the day. There were no guards about. They did not like to wander through the homes of the dead 'white devils'. Alone, gazing over the tranquil beach on which we had first landed, from which the happy home-going Americans had embarked, and on which the executions had been scheduled to take place, I allowed my grief and hatred to drain out. To gain control, I sat myself down on an old grave. Before returning to camp chores, glancing idly at the headstone, I realised how appropriate was the inscription:

*Ladies all as you pass by*
*As you are so once was I*
*As I am so you will be*
*Prepare for death and follow me*

Sweet Jesus, I thought, a prophecy?

The seer in question had been 'the dearest wife' of a colonel, in the late 1800s. How the junior wives must have suffered from her acid tongue! The jingle haunted me for the rest of the day, as no doubt she hoped it might!

Word finally got out that seven men had been executed on the beach we had landed at, in view of the camp – accused of illegal possession of radios. The most senior was the former Defence Secretary. We were also informed by our President that Sir Vandeleur Grayburn, the head of the Hong Kong and Shanghai Bank, had died in the prison hospital. We knew what they must have put him through.

71

Hardly had the camp recovered from the latest tragedy when horror struck again. News was circulated of escapes amongst the men on parole in the city. We were all delighted for them, as the escapes had been successful. However, it was not such a happy time for the companions they left behind. Two of the top bank executives were immediately brought into Stanley jail, as were four of the civil service officers. The rest, of lesser seniority, were herded into camp. The next influx were the nurses and VADs, all of whom were thankful to be with us, as life on the outside was becoming pretty basic.

The Japanese were in a ferocious mood at the violations of parole. All official supplies were stopped, as were parcels from outside friends. The two bank and two senior civil servants were given long sentences and one of the younger bank executives was sentenced to death. His wife and young son were already in our camp, and the President had to tell her the heartbreaking news. Finding life unbearable without him, she died of a broken heart. Later Lady Grayburn adopted their young son.

Guards were increased, and fabricated any excuse to use their brutality for the humiliation of the latest escapes. During this period, yet another shock wave from a daring escape within the police force in camp, engulfed us with doom. The attempt seemed ill-timed. The night after they had left they were ambushed. No details were released, but the three men were driven through the main camp road to the jail in an open lorry, pitifully beaten up. One was sentenced to be executed. The other two, rumour had it, were sentenced to life imprisonment.

There seemed no end to this dreadful time of disasters. News came through that some 2000 men from the POW camps had been loaded on the *Lisbon Maru* to work in the coal mines, on the docks and railways in Japan. Nearing Shanghai the ship was torpedoed. Most of the men were battened down below decks, so for them there was no hope. A few managed to swim to some islands off Shanghai whilst the rest of the survivors were re-shipped to Japan. This was a crippling mental blow to us all, and the terror was heightened by lack of authentic details.

The Japanese authorities were quick to use the news as propaganda, pointing out that our allies had deliberately sunk a vessel bearing the Red Cross. They had apparently disregarded the fact that the presence of Allied submarines, able to operate in the seas they claimed they held, could be some consolation. No names of any of the work force were ever released. The agony of not knowing whether members of our families, or friends, were passengers, was relieved only by infrequent messages getting through to the camp offices.

With the internment of the new crop of nurses and VADs we realised that the military hospital would be evacuated of our war wounded. Soon we heard through the bamboo wireless that a contingent of the men were being sent to Stanley jail for infractions of the evacuation rules.

Our blocks, on a higher level than the jail, overlooked an area which appeared to be an exercise yard. So far, there had never been any signs of life.

Several days after this news had been passed around, two of us were hanging the wash on the railings protecting the blocks from a sharp drop to an open space between the jail, when we noticed an untidy line of dilapidated figures, escorted by guards. On reaching this yard they started walking in a circle, while the guards formed a hollow square.

These were obviously the chaps from the military hospital. Anxious to see if we could recognise anyone, we noticed that one of the men was hopping round on his right leg, the left leg missing from the knee. It could only be Bill, a hard-swearing, hard-drinking, highly amusing chum of ours. Bill had not lost his leg in the war, but during a schoolboy rag on a train in England. To his eternal ignominy the Japanese had shot him through his right leg, hence his hospitalisation. When his discharge was imminent, he had gathered messages from the still bedridden patients and stuffed them down his tin leg, which had been returned to him. Unfortunately, it was the obvious place to look for contraband, but he felt it was worth a try! So he had earned a jail sentence, once again, minus his tin leg.

There must have been about fourteen of them all with their hands manacled behind their backs. Bill's sentence included a sadistic game played by the guards. The men exercised by shuffling round in a circle and as Bill approached a guard he would get a smart crack on his shin so that he went down landing on his stump. There was no loud shriek of pain, but knowing Bill I could easily imagine the places he was muttering as to where they could put their rifles, when he got his breath back! In painful slow motion he would raise himself up, ready for the next onslaught. From the gutteral screeches of laughter, the guards were obviously enjoying their morning duty. More internees gathered at the railings, also hoping to see someone they knew. Eventually we realised that the guards were delighted at the audience, stepping up the shuffle to a trot. We hastily disbanded from our vantage point, sickened by the pain and humiliation being inflicted. Not too many days later we were told that the exercising had stopped, and the chaps had been taken to the POW camps in Kowloon.

However, another figure familiar to most of us suddenly appeared. To the right of the yard was a 'U'-shaped, one-storeyed building, where we had seen very little activity. It was the jail's livestock area and included a pigsty, with a long trough in the middle of the 'U'. This particular morning there was a frenzy of action at the trough. The lone figure was Emil, a favourite restauranteur. A few miserable-looking sway-backed pigs were honking around him. Emil was busy flinging one ladle into the trough, while shovelling a handful into his mouth, repeating the performance as he looked around wildly, obviously watching for guards. Shades of his gastronomic menus, he really must have been starving! We formed a line against the railings with bamboo sticks. As we saw any form of authority approaching for inspection, we played a tattoo along the fence. Emil was quick to get the warning, and at least he was assured of an ample breakfast before the guards arrived.

Emil did in fact hold a British passport, which he at no time denied. However, as neither he nor his family had been actually born in Britain, he was forced to continue to run his restaurant for the convenience of the Japanese. When he eventually announced that he would no longer keep his restaurant open, and demanded that he, his wife and two small boys be interned in our camp, he was sent to jail for a short period of rehabilitation. Eventually he was allowed to rejoin the family, all of whom were living in the town with so-called non-Allies. Rugged as our camp was, the hardships of coping in the town were formidable.

The entertainment committee had decided on their first production. The choice was extremely ambitious, but it had the advantage of a cast of only four players, and the minimum of scenery. *Private Lives*! The audacity caused some caustic comments in theatrical circles! The selection of the two principals was an inspiration – Rick and his lovely Janie!

Permission had been granted for the plays provided the scripts were first vetted by the Japanese. Concerts and revues would be allowed if inoffensive! The Japanese interpreter selected Della to collaborate over the censorship of the productions to be staged in St Stephen's Hall.

*Private Lives* was the test case. The lines referring to the vast size of China compared with Japan, were diplomatically omitted before vetting. Depending on the audience not including any of the senior Japanese, who all spoke and understood English, the lines referring to the two countries would be included!

A three-night extension of curfew was allowed for performances. Rehearsals were in full swing, suitable clothing, and stage-setting rounded up by eager helpers.

The auditorium had only four rows of chairs, the first row reserved for camp dignitaries. Otherwise it was standing room only, and the producer with a few friends in the gallery.

There was great excitement through the camp. The thrill of a late night curfew, and a real live entertainment, be it amateur, was a welcome break in the monotony. On the first night the hall was bursting its seams. The first row was graced by the Japanese commandant of our camp, Victoria, and other Japanese dignitaries and their staff – most of the senior

Japanese, who, as I say, spoke and understood English, no doubt knew the play. Our camp committee and other senior citizens filled the next couple of rows – then it was first come. It was almost a gay and happy feeling, a gala occasion with every one of us determined to enjoy our evening.

The play was received rapturously. Rick and Janie were absolutely splendid. Even the sceptical pundits who had foretold its doom were lavish in their praise. The second and third nights we were informed that Commandant Tanaka and his retinue had declined their invitations. The deleted lines were included in the right context. The audiences howled with delight, banging tins together, stamping whatever footwear, if any, they possess.

Dizzy with success, the committee started planning their next smash hit. Light reviews were staged, frothy shorts, which had a bit of cabaret dancing included, whilst the producer and director mulled over the next full-length performances.

A delighted Tanaka informed our President that he would, in future, be inviting other senior citizens of HIM the Emperor to attend our performances. No doubt it was a novelty from Kabuki, but a shower of cold water on the citizens of the camp! His enthusiasm, however, did wane. There were far more sophisticated forms of entertainment in the big city of Victoria. This was an enormous relief to everyone. The committee had to be a bit wary, as he was inclined to suddenly announce that he intended watching a performance, sometimes only with his own staff, occasionally with friends from the city. This made for hasty re-reading of scripts should it be a play, just to make sure that any scurrilous insult on HIM the Emperor, or even our own Japanese guardians, was deleted.

The main hall of St Stephen's was ideal for most forms of entertainment, with a large stage at the north end. The dressing rooms had been allocated as living quarters, However, there was a wide enough corridor behind the stage for impromptu dressing rooms. One area could be curtained off for the boys and another for the girls. As there were at least two handsomely armed guards prowling and peering during performances, segregation was really hardly necessary!

It was tricky work trying to dress or undress almost elbow to elbow, particularly as the guards were getting bolder and more familiar with the gals, and several of us had, eventually, to complain at their attempts to be friendly with a quick pinch or nick with their bayonets. We had a couple of near disasters, when we had to appear before the No. 2 officer in charge, to have our interpreter smooth things out. If they thought we were poking Charlie at them they would give us a painful enough slap across the backside. We all tried to keep the atmosphere as carefree as possible, and although the odd guard was fascinated watching rehearsals, they made sure no senior officer was lurking around.

Rehearsals could not monopolise the hall, which was in great demand for lectures, classes, community singing and musical evenings. But somehow we managed to rehearse in sections, and put the whole together at dress rehearsal! The audiences were almost part of the show, vociferous in their appreciation, catcalls and advice to the performers if there was a hitch or a cue missed! Each time the entertainment became more polished. It was tremendous fun being auditioned, scouring around for props and suitable costumes. Learning lines and attending long rehearsals on a low-calorie diet could be exhausting, but there was never any lack of enthusiasm. Our committee became more and more ambitious. Music was put together to suit the performances, and we had a professional choreographer who staged some dreamy ballets. The most unexpected people turned out to be natural actors, dancers and comics.

Carole Bateman, our ballet mistress and choreographer, was famous in Shanghai for her school of ballet during the city's days of international splendour. Her star pupil, whom Carol always maintained would achieve the ultimate accolade in the world of ballet, was Margot Fonteyn. It was natural for Carol to be on the entertainment committee. For their next production they decided to select culture! However, it was thought that if the audiences were to be submitted to culture let it be the light-hearted variety, *A Midsummer Night's Dream*. The choice was greeted with mixed enthusiasm. There was a lot of script to memorise, and most of the applicants for auditioning had gained their only experience in school plays. Since I had portrayed Puck quite a few times in my schooldays, the battle of the dialogue was already half won, and so the role was mine! Fortunately by this time, along with the other misshapen young women, my balloon-like proportions had subsided; most of us were now below normal weight.

Gruelling rehearsals began most afternoons. For my entrance 'leap' on stage, Carol subjected me to sessions of trying to land gracefully from hummock to ground, without endangering the collapse of nearby buildings! Obsessed as I was with these acrobatics, Mother would have to restrain me from falling out of my camp-cot some nights, whilst dreaming of Carol firmly telling me to try once more! Carol finally decided the leap was as ready as it would ever be, and fervently hoped the stage would stand up to the onslaught.

Having got through the hillside ordeals, and with first night only two nights away, Carol placed me on stage. The leap was to be from the top of a short step-ladder in the wings. This was held by two stalwart stage hands. After several attempts, fraught with nervousness, Carol was satisfied that I would land daintily at the feet of Oberon.

The morning of our first performance was cold and wet. The basis of Puck's costume was a singlet, briefs and a pair of streaky-dyed hospital stockings. Overall, leaves gathered from the hillside had to be tacked on, newly gathered, each day – true act of devotion to the arts. A couple of chums voted to help on the early morning leaf-picking, Apart from it being a chilly job, we were liable to bump into a disgruntled guard, curious to know what we were doing abroad so early.

Ages before the curtain rose at 6p.m. on THE night, my helpers had firmly covered me with a shroud of cold wet leaves, adding to the chill of stage-fright! The step-ladder was in position, the play was on. My stockinged feet were so cold they threatened to anaesthetise my lower limbs, so having perched me atop the ladder, a kindly stalwart, of roughly six feet, suggested my putting on his welfare-boots to keep me warm while I was waiting for my cue! Not wanting to be churlish I slid my feet into this very heavy and rather grubby footwear.

The audience was the kind all actors must dream about. Like them, completely engrossed in the play, I hardly felt the gentle shake of the ladder breaking the spell. There was scarcely time to scramble to my feet when my cue thundered across the stage, 'Where is my gentle Puck?'

I leapt, landing roughly where touchdown was, but with a resounding thud. One large black welfare-boot hit the deck, bouncing into the front row, mercifully missing our august guests! The other boot, having taken to the air during my descent, dropped heavily on Oberon's right shoulder, completely paralysing the poor fellow.

A momentary hideous silence followed, in which I tried to utter my reply. Then came the roars. The audience was convulsed, thumping each other with howls of laughter. Carol gestured wildly from the wings and a couple of little pixies scuttled on to remove the offending boot, scrabbling for the honour of taking it off!

Somehow the show went on. The players reacting to my ghastly goof, began hamming it up too. Bottom successfully used his two fingers, depicting the crack in the wall with that famous Churchillian gesture! So ended the opening night, with raucous shouts through the whole performance!

Cast and friends, exhausted and elated, gathered on stage behind the final curtain, and Carol joined us with the helpers and dressers, all sounding very grand. Everyone had brought some morsel saved from rations or parcels, and someone produced half mugs of hot chocolate, rather diluted, but quite delicious. I was fortunately forgiven for my ruinous entrance which, to my horror, the rest of the cast wanted incorporated into the remaining performances. Gratefully, neither Carol nor Oberon thought it would be a good idea, as it could have had disastrous results and at the following two performances I remained strictly bootless, and the play went according to the script. My clodhopping debut earned me an addition to 'Bring-the-bottle-kid'. To my shame my nickname was lengthened to 'Bring-the-bottle-and-boots'.

# 5

One of the strictest rules we were ordered to observe was that when confronted by a sentry on duty, or indeed any Japanese guard or officer we were obliged to bow three times. This servility became farcical. The extensive distribution of guards throughout the camp, and our continuous trekking between the widely spread camp areas made a shambles of this supposed act of 'courtesy'.

Dottie was one of our anti-establishment inmates – mid forties, tall, deceptively serene-looking, she was constantly waging war against useless rules, and pinpricks! She decided one morning she would try out an experiment. She planned to circulate all sentry points, as often as possible, during which time she would also meet the odd guard ambling around, and see who would tire of the bowing first. We were not about to encourage her; it seemed a risky manoeuvre, especially with the vicious looking Bayonet-Boy, who might just get the picture after her second or third encounter.

But no amount of dissuasion was accepted. This was her mission, and she intended to carry it out. Her first stop would be Humpty Dumpty, at the end of our block. He was one of the older guards, an unforbidding-faced little character. He was enchanted by the younger children who used to tease him, frequently chanting, 'Filthy Japaneeeseees' with wide innocent smiles, hands held out for the odd goodie he might have in his pockets.

The experiment began and we all prayed the Happy Travelling Buddah would be with her. A couple of hours later, hot but triumphant, Dottie dragged herself to her camp-cot and collapsed! That evening a notice on the bulletin board directed that in future, only one bow was required to all Japanese personnel. No explanations were given, but one taken! Dottie got a bonus from her blockmates. Before lights out she was presented with a steaming mug of tea with a generous lacing of condensed milk. What bliss!

Some weeks later the Happy Travelling Buddahs were holidaying elsewhere when Peg, one of my old chums, always optimistic and ready with her area rumours, joined me for a stroll via Siberia. Her billet was in the Indian quarters, and we would try to meet several evenings a week to mull over the day's events. Our first sentry post was usually manned after evening meal by a disgusting little brute nicknamed Pisspot. The path we took to connect with via Siberia was quiet, with heavy undergrowth all down the right. Once we had navigated past Pisspot we had a free run without sentries for about a mile.

As we neared Pisspot it was obvious that he was honouring his nickname, back turned to us, into the bushes. Seeing that he was taking time out, we speeded by, no bows. There was a bellow and a beckoning for us to return, whilst he fumbled with his flies. Before I was aware of any movement from him there was a mighty backhander across my face. The pain flooded my brain, and signalled my right hand to retaliate. In the few seconds it took Pisspot to realise the enormity of the insult, Peg and I bolted full pelt over the side of the path into the deeper undergrowth.

There was no further bellowing as we stumbled our way through the bushes, tripping over one or two romancing couples. We made the safety of the blocks, and I shooed Peg off home. My face was very hot and red too! I discovered that there was some blood on my mouth where my lips had obviously come in contact with my teeth. While still seething with the indignity of the attack, before my senses began to crawl with fear at the consequences of my automatic return slap, I contacted poor Phil for advice.

Phil was naturally horrified, and after going over the best way to tackle any probable outcome, he suggested I wait with him to see if there was to be an immediate order for the arrest of the culprit. By this time my indignation had dwindled considerably. Curfew came, still nothing. Phil went to collect the evening's bulletin board. No ominous notice. We felt the danger point had passed, or rather Phil did, and reassuringly sent me back to our room. Mother was concerned at the state of my face, as were my room mates. Sensibly no questions were asked. Not even able to swallow my final mug of 'gnat's pee', I rolled into my blanket, only to spend most of the night visiting the lavatory.

A message came from Phil after roll-call that he too had spent the night waiting for the fireworks. Phil sent word to me that I was posted on the sick list for roll-call and was to remain out of sight. Mother swathed my rapidly swelling face in a 'toothache' towel, but how to disguise my eye, which was developing into a real shiner was a problem. A pair of dark glasses were borrowed. I had no intention of appearing in public, but the glasses did help the morale. Luckily it was the season for sunglasses, so not an uncommon sight if I had to go out of the room.

The next twenty-four hours, indeed for two more days, I drifted about the room in a haze of subdued terror. The old tummy was very wobbly, anticipating Phil's arrival with the arrest guard party. Mother alternated between crowd-mingling for any rumours circulating reference an 'incident' involving guard-baiting, and trying to contact either Phil or Joyce. Having opted-out of camp duties until the situation was resolved I was thankful when Joyce came over finally after the admin office had closed, to report that there was still no word from Up-The-Hill of any molestation of guards! Both she and Phil decided the crisis passed.

Though I couldn't be complacent about the un-canny silence from on high, I prayed that my brush with Pisspot had been sufficiently humiliating to him not to take the chance of making trouble.

The Happy Travelling Buddahs were thankfully back on my side. Phil could only deduce that Pisspot had not reported his mauling because of loss of face. Phil himself had plodded past the particular sentry post both following evenings, and told me there had been a change of guard. Praying my fervent thanks, I made a solemn promise not to allow my rebellious self to be provoked ever, ever again. I was even happy to wrestle with my enemy the taro plant again.

While the hospital was being issued with a supply of condoms from the main government hospital in Pok-Fulam the staff were able to distribute them, as they thought fair enough, to married couples.

Romances were flourishing and these items were in great demand; they could be exchanged for the most essential commodity, food. The going price was a tin of bully beef or condensed milk. However, when the hospital supply came to a sudden halt, the value greatly increased! Most of the younger children scoured areas described as likely for pollination, finding the odd balloon. Prompted by the parents, our authorities appealed to the lovers for discretion. Privacy being at such a premium, even the one empty grave, always ready for the cemetery, became a trysting place. There was sometimes a roster for the privilege, and if it could be arranged, someone would keep a lookout for the marauding guard who might appear on the horizon with a view to quizzing the territory. This was very infrequent, the cemetery being a bad joss place for the living.

The handicaps of adjusting to life were severest amongst the older people. The graveyard took its share of internees. Most of the very badly needed drugs were smuggled in, not always successfully.

The camp dentist eventually managed to set up his surgery. Sam was a terrific person, large and bear-like, gentle and always helpful. With the help of his gallant wife, he toiled long hours to help stop toothache and to save his patients' teeth whenever possible. Like the doctors' and nurses' it was a gruelling job.

One of the unpleasant early experiences was when the Japanese set up vaccination centres. We were lined up by numbers for a needle thrust in the arm and if you were too far down the line the needles could be exceedingly blunt, and in some cases set up a painful infection. We were never told exactly what these jabs were for and we wholeheartedly dreaded both the unknown quantity and being at the mercy of these medical ministrations. After a series of jab-lines, the Japanese either ran out of vaccine or got bored with the procedure. Perhaps the stiff-upper-lipped Britisher didn't squawk loudly enough. Before the drill was behind us the idea was to either make the head of the line of a top few, or dribble away from the end, hopefully, which sometimes worked!

Our own medics were not happy with the immunisation idea as there was always a terrible chance of starting up a bodily infection through a dirty, or too well-used needle, which would require antibiotics, which were all too rare to come by.

The New Year was greeted with a surge of optimism. Even the guards looked less menacing. There was a fresh spate of happy rumours; no foundations other than wishes: mail between our camp and the POWs' camps would perhaps be allowed. The use of the lovely Tweed Bay beach for summer relaxation? Red Cross parcels, so long promised? Letters from our families at home? The only resolutions that could be made, and possibly truthfully kept, were faith in a swift and victorious end to the global war.

A visit from a Swiss national, representing the Red Cross, appeared on the bulletin board just after the New Year had started on its usual daily round. All internees were to be on parade, no one was to approach the gentleman. Our own committee would be allowed to join the Japanese entourage whilst the Swiss gentleman made his tour of inspection. He arrived, a rather short, grey-haired man with steel-rimmed spectacles. He was so thin. Somehow one imagined that the 'lucky' ones living outside would be bursting with fleshy health! Many of the older businessmen in camp recognised him as a local resident.

The poor chap was whisked around the camp with grave solemnity. He had only to look at the dishevelled mob lining the route to draw his own conclusions. We had been asked very firmly by our President not to cause any incident by a noisy demonstration. His seemingly pointless tour did, however, raise once again the speculation that it could herald a load of Red Cross parcels, which did in fact materialise eventually. Seven and a half of these luxuries over the three and a half years were distributed before the source petered out.

The first parcel was a Red-Cross-Red-Letter-Day. The cheering resounded through camp as we clamoured round the collection points and carted off our prize. It was unbelievable to see those dreamed-of tins of bully beef, chocolate, soap, and even an occasional packet of cigarettes. The cigarettes, of course, were like gold bars, as they could be swapped for the nicotine maniac's bar of chocolate, or even a tin of food. There was one item included which caused much merriment, a tin of creamed RICE! Not to be despised, but rather ironical! We all tried to eke out the wonderful, almost forgotten tastes, but more often greed won the day, or rather the evening, with that last brew of tea! As it happened, many of the subsequent parcels were rifled en route to the camp, mostly of cigarettes which gradually appeared for sale by the Blacks! It was incredible to most of us how many of the older citizens kept their parcels practically intact until news of the next issue's arrival!

But most of us donated the creamed rice to the hospital, which in turn shared it with the babies. One rather large boy arrived on parcel day. Needless to say he was nicknamed Bully Boy – the babies were all in splendid health, and after being weaned thrived on the camp menu! Nature is surely a canny character. Fortunately, as the weather was predominantly hot, not too many clothes were needed – the camp tailors were able to make garments out of the clothes donated by the people who had come in from their homes on the island. Woollen cardigans were unpicked and reknitted into baby clothes for the winter. Nappies were in very short supply as the hospital needed white garments for dressings and bandages. However, the very young looked cute in their patterned nappies. The mums were rationed as to clothing for their young, especially as the kids already in camp were growing normally, and they also had to be clothed! The most accomplished tailors were the Jesuit priests – very handy with the needle. They were also great clog makers, when they got an allocation of wood – not the most comfortable footwear in the winter, which was, in Hong Kong, thankfully not too long.

The end of the first year was looming up. Dreams of repatriation faded as we began to realise this had never really been programmed for the British subjects. We were, after all, expected to and did take this annexation of British soil as a temporary plight. The majority of us never for a moment considered that the war would not end in victory for the Allies. No bearers of ill wind were taken seriously, just treated with contempt.

The Blacks were flourishing for those still with ready cash. Otherwise preference was given to good credit customers, bankers, government servants and old established companies. Interests were high, but to a certain extent so were the risks involved. The King

Pin was fireproof, the little guys occasionally raided, principally some felt as a screen. No matter, they catered in precious necessities.

Christmas Day of 1942 would not be a joyous one for any of us. For many it was a sad and bitter time, crowded with memories of family and friends who had not survived December 25, 1941.

Extension of curfew was granted for carol singing and church services. Cards were drawn for special friends. One camp wit had drawn a rising sun, known as the poached egg in the East corner, bearing the message:

'Happy-crappy'
'Ditto-shitto'

This was circulated; the receiver initialled it and sent it on to whomsoever they wished. Not exactly a message of peace and goodwill, but it caused a lot of laughs, and in some cases added ditties!

The cooks outdid themselves for Christmas dinner; their famous pasties seemed to have a special flavour. We got together with our favourite chums, pooling our rations, adding a few tasty 'afters' we had hoarded for a party.

Tom, one of our inveterate under-the-wire foragers, produced some mandarin oranges and a couple of bottles of rice wine. He was a compact man of medium height, dark red hair, and a devotion to the dangerous role he had undertaken, which made him wary of being too friendly. He had been 'putting down' bottles of rice wine for various friends for such an event, but through the year, many of them had popped their corks, so that we relied on his expertly brewed vintage 1941 as the safest drink! We had to be extra vigilant when curfew was extended, for that was when off-duty Japanese would roam the camp, looking for trouble. They suspected there was some liquor about the camp, and having stoked themselves up in their billets, were decidely the worse for booze, so it was a good idea for we females to keep out of sight and for the chaps not to get in their way.

Christmas holidays over, the schools reopened. The library went into full swing and the small communal plots of vegetable gardens began to produce. Tomatoes and greens were rightly kept for the hospital and the children, but the garlic was added to the daily fare and livened it up tastewise.

Firewood for our home-made private cookers was getting difficult to scrounge round the hillsides. Mysteriously the parquet flooring in large sections of the camp buildings began to disappear! Joyce arrived one morning for library duty to find the main hall completely stripped of its flooring. Our premises, shut off behind the bar, were still intact. Joyce appealed to the library committee for permission to remove our flooring before someone else claimed it. So with the committee's blessing and share of the dividend, we took it in turns to prise up the boards, keeping watch for the patrolling guards forever sticking their buck teeth into our business. Undoubtedly Japanese headquarters knew what was going on, but had turned the proverbial blind eye. A period of harmless harmony, however short, was less disruptive in their dealings with this unpredictable rabble!

Then came an unsettling rumour that another radio was active. After the first disaster only furtive references to the truth of this were made. Andrew cautiously mentioned that our authorities were very disturbed, as the original squealer had not as yet been pinpointed. The inevitable message of ill tidings appeared on the bulletin board, confined to quarters. The radio hunt was on. Once again the Gendarmerie bullies were sent in to comb the camp. As before they concentrated on one particular area, an obvious tip-off. Hours of dry-mouthed anxiety, then word was whispered through the camp. The radio had been found. It had been concealed in an old battered bucket half-filled with washing water. There was a false bottom, not apparently obvious at all. The bully boys twice missed the location, having stripped several quarters in the part of the camp they were sure was the hiding place. As they passed the bucket again, in a raging fury one of them kicked it off the stoop; thus they found their prize.

The three men sharing the tiny quarter to which the bucket belonged were dragged off to Gendarmerie HQ. We learned that having been brutally manhandled they were taken into the jail, where they received the inevitable sentence. However, as there was no immediate confirmation that the executions had been carried out, the chance of a mythical life sentence gave some hope. We had word that one of the senior bank executives had died in jail, and that there were a group of POWs from Kowloon awaiting trial for ignoring the ban on radio messages to the outside world. The whole camp was in a nasty and restless mood. We seemed to be waiting for the spark to set the bonfire alight.

Our safety valve, strangely enough, was the tantalising drone of night-flying aircraft. These, we were assured, were Allied planes on missions in China. Supporting this assurance was an order to return to our quarters on hearing these aircraft; cheering news indeed.

Towards the end of January there was a lull in the now familiar sound of planes. Penny and Maggie, whose billet was in one of the delightful bungalows on the St Stephen plateau, suggested that Peg and I have a happy couple of hours of bridge. There was a garage attached to the bungalow which the occupants used as a community centre, so it was arranged that Peg and I collect our morning meal and take it up to pool it for the bridge session. Maggie said she had some curry paste which she would drop into the stew, and Peg and I had a banana each to donate for the dessert.

The four of us had settled down to a good old exchange of news, views and gossip before the bridge game started when there was a distinct hum of aircraft. As we listened the rest of those still in the bungalow came out to strain their eyes and ears to the sky. The whining was definitely becoming louder and nearer. Penny said it would be a good idea if Peg and I got back to our quarters fast; we could return for the meal and game when all was clear.

Hurrying down a slight bank, the quickest way to the road we had to cross, there were several thrrumps towards the city, but getting closer. Fatso, the rotund ball of yellow and khaki, perched on top of hoop-shaped legs, was the sentry on duty at the path leading to the road. He frantically gestured us to dive under a small leafy tree on our right. The deafening explosions meant business. Fatso joined us, crouching beside Peg, nervously lighting a cigarette. Next to me was a rough war grave, with a good sized piece of rock at the head. Gunfire grew very close and clear, and as we instinctively covered our heads between our knees there was a mighty explosion. Various lumps of debris hurtled over the area, dislodging the gravestone and sending a shower of quite painful earth and stones in our direction.

There was a sudden awful quiet before we could shake ourselves of rubble, then Fatso was screeching at us to beat it across the road. As he got up to dive back to his box he neatly stubbed his cigarette out on the back of Peg's hand.

We made the security of my block, our clogs under our arms. Others like ourselves were racing like startled bunnies for their own quarters. Brave guards, now that the 'raid' was over, were officiously waving their rifles about and yelling maniacally. Amid the confusion Peg came back with me to the room. Mother was shaken at our decoration of dust, leaves and some minor scratches.

The devastating news was released. The bungalow we had left so light-heartedly had a direct hit. Fourteen of the internees had been killed, including our two bridge partners, and several people had been badly injured. A sickening end to what was to have been a cheerful day. It was a miracle that the bungalow was the only casualty. The St Stephen's area was a crowded one, which included the Japanese headquarters – unharmed, probably a blessing as there would undoubtedly have been reprisals against the camp. As it was everyone was confined to quarters until further notice. This type of upheaval always precipitated unwanted changes, keeping everyone on edge.

Tony came into our room to say he had also been near bungalow 14, and was sure he had heard ground fire from the road under the bungalow. He had also seen the plane come down quite low and then turn sharply into the sky – he said it definitely had American markings. There was no further sound of planes or bombs.

We learned that against all codes of war, the Japanese had stationed an anti-aircraft gun on the road directly under the bungalow, from which they were firing at the aircraft. There was nothing to indicate that the area over which the planes were flying was an internment camp. Whereas the Japanese barracks on the opposite hill, which was also firing its guns, was obviously a military position. Our President made pressing demands that a Red Cross be painted, at least on the hospital grounds.

The camp was in a morass of despair. It was many days after the funeral of our companions that Peg and I returned to the tree to replace the rocky headstone, or what was left of it, on the unmarked grave. Our sorrow was coupled with a sense of mixed blessings that the war had definitely come closer to us. We were prepared to be targets if it meant the end would be quick and soon. Meanwhile, messages came through the bamboo wireless that the POW camps in Kowloon had been shaken up, but happily there were no serious casualties.

We had so many interesting people amongst us. There was a professor of languages, and several of us enrolled in his Spanish classes. One of my friends was a charming Russian artist. He offered to teach me his mother tongue, which appealed enormously. The classes were conversational, paper being a scarcity. Alex started my classes with grave devotion, but he was extremely temperamental. Weeks would go by when he was not in the mood. Thus I didn't get very far, nor become very fluent!

Two other popular gentlemen were One-Armed Sutton, advisor to Sun Yat Sen, and Two-Gun Cohen, bodyguard to the same Chinese statesman. Both

Sutton and Cohen were expert bridge players, always willing to coach aspiring Culbertsons. Cohen was brilliant at card tricks, and kept us enthralled many an evening. He could also deal any hand one asked for. As no stakes were involved one was in honour bound to play to the best of one's ability, no fooling around. Sadly, General Sutton – his rank in the Chinese Army – died in camp. Inactivity, ill health and the lack of news broke his will to live. Two-Gun, on the other hand, carried on gamely, until one day the Gendarmerie dragged him off to their headquarters. No reasons were given and no one expected to see him returned to camp. A long spell passed before he limped back, badly scarred and partially crippled. He never spoke of his session with the bully boys, just took up life as normally as possible. We had so much fun watching his sleight of hand performances. None of us ever solved the magic of his dealing!

Joyce had a problem. It was hard to believe because she was always so imperturbable, moving calmly through camp life, cheerful, sympathetic, the golden-haired sister figure. Her problem was a universal one, lack of ready cash. Her mother, whom we all called Mama-T, was losing weight and energy to an alarming degree, and her ready quips and lavish hospitality with the convivial mug of warmth to revive a flagging spirit were becoming an effort. She was quite an old lady and Joyce was devoted to her. Even though Joyce had been able to provide extras with her small amount of dollars, she needed a real sum of money to be able to get a supply of vitamin pills from the Blacks.

The solution was a resourceful, if delicate one. She had two gold-filled molars, and if she could persuade

97

Sam to remove them, there was her bargaining point. After a long chat with me, it was decided that we would discuss the operation with Sam. He was most understanding, but reluctant to pull two healthy teeth. There was the danger of excessive bleeding. He spent a half hour of his off-duty that evening examining the two money bags and, after a lot of thought, reluctantly agreed to have a go at one tooth, the next day, again in his free time.

We arrived for the appointment, Joyce thrilled with the idea of her potential wealth, and me in a state of the vapours! Sam began his probing while I clung onto her shoulders as if she were my lifebelt. Out came the filling; the tooth was hollow, and declared a dead one. Sam rapidly put a chunk of dental cement in its place, and with enthusiasm launched on the second tooth. This was not so obliging. He gave it a quick hard yank. Joyce squirmed in the chair, while I hung on so tight that she was practically strangling! In the end there was hardly any blood, Sam jubilant, his wife mopping. As Joyce teetered out of the room, triumphantly holding her booty, a few curious characters who had been peering through the window, raised a hearty hurrah!

'Now,' lisped Joyce through a rather swollen tongue, 'to the Blacks for the vits!'

Mama-T was almost in a state of collapse when she discovered where the little blue pills had arrived from, but dutifully took her daily quota while they lasted!

Shortly after the 'rape-of-the-gold-teeth', as Mama-T forever referred to her pill session, I developed a disfiguring cyst on my right jaw bone. The unsightly lump climbed up to my ear lobe. No matter how I tried to ignore the lump, it got larger, and began to be painful. Down to the hospital, this time Joyce firmly clutching me. My friendly doctor told me that it must be lanced. Listening in a state of panic to his assurance that he would be able to use an anaesthetic, the date was made. Everyone made clucking noises; it was nothing to get in a lather about, I wouldn't feel a thing. How right they were!

On the day arranged I presented myself at the operating theatre. Edith, one of the nurses, prepared my face. The doctor appeared and chatted away to me, explaining what he was about to do while Edith smeared something on the offending lump. I noticed that there were a couple of our stalwart police lads, who were volunteer orderlies, standing casually by the operating table, and wondered vaguely why they were there. After I had climbed onto the table one of the lads held my shoulders gently, the other my legs. Seeing the doctor advancing, I firmly screwed my eyes tightly shut, and being a devout coward, accommodatingly fainted as the knife struck! No worries, it was all over by the time I came to. Edith dressed the wound, then handed me the panacea for all discomforts, the welcome mug of tea, and it was sweet!

My cowardice paid off. Another young woman had the same trouble. Unfortunately a nerve had been nicked and her mouth had to be wired to try and help the drooping side. No fault of the doctor, she had been too brave. Remaining conscious, as of course there was no anaesthetic for such a minor operation, she had unavoidably jerked at the wrong moment.

Joyce was waiting to escort me back with the exciting news that yet another Red Cross parcel was waiting collection. As before this was a tremendous morale booster. Against all rules the packers of the parcels would leave the odd message of hope inside the parcel. So, we learned afterwards, people did know we were here. Perhaps our messages had already been delivered by our American friends, giving cheer to our families.

# 6

Our theatricals were becoming very popular. Two more plays had been staged and Carol was planning her first ballet. She desperately wished that her partner of the ballet and dance school in Shanghai was in camp to help her. The task Carol had set herself was monumental, even with the involvement of such helpful and tremendous talent in the art world of Hong Kong at hand. All forms of entertainment were widely encouraged. Musical evenings, poetry and play readings. Bridge sessions were arranged, and classes to teach bridge were available. There was no doubt that the stage shows were becoming more sophisticated, despite the difficulty in producing suitable props and costumes. Everyone interested was catered for, either in helping to produce or teaching people eager to learn.

The population, too, was increasing. Extra mouths to feed did not amuse the Japanese who finally issued the following order: 'Fornication between married couples and very good friends is permitted – however as most of the internees are NOT very good friends this practice must STOP forthwith.'

As one cuckold observed wryly, 'They should have qualified "married couples" as those who *legally* belong together!'

This latest 'order' was backed up with the hard facts that no extra rations would be provided for the newcomers. Human nature tended to ignore ridiculous sentiment; but the obvious hideaway for romancing, the roof tops, was declared taboo! The cemetery had two graves usually ready – but these could only be used in daylight for obvious reasons. They were not very popular, but had been known to be used, a lookout at each of the two entrances with a noisy signal of some sort arranged by both parties. It was pretty gruesome and after a while the idea was abandoned.

After the success of our Shakespearean culture the committee decided to do something less demanding. *Lilies of the Field* seemed to be the obvious choice, as there was only one stage setting, which meant no scene shifting.

So weeks of rehearsals, battling with the inter-preters, bulling our way through the censorship, the play was ready to be launched. *Lilies of the Field* was not madly exciting, but light, airy and not too much concentration was required to learn the lines.

The big scene was the tea party. For this our cast planned to stun the audience by producing real cakes and sandwiches, to be arrayed on a cakestand made by one of the camp carpenters. We had bribed a cook with a few cigarettes saved by our smokers in the cast (with great self-denial) to bake us a cake, if we provided the rice flour. The director suggested that we nibble daintily, leaving enough of the goodies to do for the next two nights, in case our collective offerings could not be repeated.

Opening night – a full house was reported. Our Camp Commandant, his officers, and with them in the front row the Chief Commandant of all POWs

and the internment camp. There was also a sprink-
ling of those white-faces still living outside the camp.
Backstage were the usually scruffy guards sloping
around, peering into the makeshift dressing rooms,
or flipping through the few magazines we had
managed to collect for the drawing room scene.

The reception as the curtain went up was flatter-
ingly enthusiastic. We romped through the first two
acts, hardly able to wait for the tea party! The curtain
rang down amongst much foot stomping and
applause, while we bustled about arranging the
centrepiece, the cakestand in the next act. There were
tasty little rice biscuits spread with home-made peanut butter, delicious cup cakes spotted with orange
peel or banana slices, and the breathtaking rice loaf,
spread on three sides with a chocolate icing for the
benefit of the audience, the cocoa and some parcel
butter generously donated by our leading man! As
there was no more cocoa for icing a cake each night
we agreed to save this masterpiece for the final
performance! The stage was set. The director, rounding us up, sent the prompter to give a last minute
check on the centrepiece. We were all drooling at the
thought of a snack in the next act. The prompter
returned backstage white with fury, thrusting the
director, who was giving us a few final words of
encouragement, into the wings. With just about three
minutes to go before curtain-up, there were four of
the guards lounging in the chairs surrounding the all-
important cakestand, munching happily on our carefully decorated tea party fare! No amount of per-
suasion to leave the scene had any effect, but just
caused much merriment. By this time the assembled
cast were adding to the director's protestations, to no
avail. The saboteurs continued to wreck the highlight

of the act.

The audience were getting restless: cat-calls, whistles, shouts of 'We'll miss our supper'. It was quite chaotic, our uninvited guests determined to finish the feast. There was a hush in the audience, and we heard our gallant director apologise for the delay, adding that there had been a slight hitch – the caterers had not arrived!

After much rattling of their rifles, the guards sauntered off stage, leaving us the debris. The tea party would have to be played without the centrepiece. It was a somewhat deflated act, lines were forgotten, the prompter kept busy, but the audience, sensing something untoward had happened, remained dramatically silent during the vapid dialogue, with just the odd embarrassed guffaw.

The last line was given a thunderous ovation, and we took our bows in an untidy daze!

A backstage conference was held as to how we could plan our revenge. The director had a brilliant idea for the second night. We would scrounge sufficient ingredients to concoct one large 'chocolate' cake. The hospital would be coerced into supplying a very generous amount of tasteless as possible laxative, the top would be decorated with a few banana slices, interspersed with emetic pills dyed with mercuricome with pieces of precious wong tong around the outside and Red Cross parcel sugar over the top. No other eats at all.

It was arranged for a stagehand to feign elaborate plans to guard the cake. Once again the centrepiece was placed lovingly on stage. The foursome of guards appeared, proceeded to cut and devour the enormous cake. The cast put up the best performance of our entire careers, hissing, wailing and wringing our hands! The curtain went up, and in some mysterious way, as can happen on these occasions, the audience got the picture!

The act was hilarious, every line and every move greeted with loud clapping. As we got ourselves ready to trundle back to quarters, a small band of admirers, friends and stagehands announced that they had canvassed around the theatre enthusiasts, who in turn had rallied with promises of quite an amazing selection of goodies for our last night. Prompted by what we all hoped would not 'backfire' on us (the director's pun), it was the joke of the year!

That third, and successful, tea party scene must have been a record for any stage performance! There were four new alert-looking guards in place of our former trustees, for the last night who gave the stage a wide berth, not even bothering to inspect the cakestand. We tucked in not so daintily; in fact the star of the show was so engrossed in savouring his cupcake that he missed his punch line, which was supplied by a delighted audience who had seen most of the performances!

Our director did some tactful questioning around the hospital. We learned with much glee that the hospital had been ordered to send Japanese head-quarters a large supply of something to stop the trots and vomiting. Revenge was indeed sweet!

Our preoccupation with food was like a disease. We never tired of talking recipes, recalling some culinary delight – most of the recipes were related to sweets, making fudge, fancy ice creams and one intrepid cordon bleu cook gave 'cooking lessons'. This was to read out the ingredients for a certain dish, the method of cooking it, and the sauces and garnishings that accompanied it! I'm afraid these little sessions

105

didn't last long. They got too tantalising and tummy-rumbling!

The older people discussed the wonderful binges they had been on, and the pros and cons of hangover remedies! Some of them sounded pretty grim. The cardinal sin, an unwritten law by which all abided, was never ever to steal food. As there were no facilities for locking up a larder, most of us kept our precious standbys in the space provided by mutual agreement, in our rooms. One day a henious crime was committed in Block 4. Myra had put a tin lid of rice grains to dry out, on the low wall opposite the ground floor room which she shared with her four room-mates. She was going to experiment making popcorn-rice. The wall was in easy access of people passing back and forth on their various day's business. Myra was taking a kindergarten class in the club hall. When she returned an obvious large handful of the rice was missing. No one had noticed the theft, but we were all naturally concerned.

The next day Myra followed the same pattern, and a look-out was posted in an unobtrusive corner of the room. Presently Humpty Dumpty was seen trundling up the road, a small child held by each hand. The children were howling, fractious and reluctant. One of the cooks, busy stoking the fire under our morning meal, asked in his pidgin-Japanese what the problem was. By much use of handsigns and pidgin conversation, it transpired that these two little monsters had been, for the second day, playing at the back of his post, and the game, as the day before, had ended in hair pulling and general small child quarrelling. Humpty Dumpty had parted them to haul them to their quarters. Sauntering back to his post he passed the precious lid of rice, and nonchalantly scooped up a handful of rice grains, stuffing them in his mouth. Well . . . the culprit was found. Much to the relief of us all it was only Humpty Dumpty, who was probably as hungry as we were! Naturally there could be no reprisals, but no more lids of anything were left on that wall again!

Myra had her kindergarten classes twice a week – for just an hour. They were usually through by the time the library opened, and another group took over part of the hall for whatever activity they had arranged. The best time for special messages about nightly rendezvous amongst the men who were planning smuggling, or news swapping operations, was then. The information would be passed to us in the library, to be handed out in a book specified by a borrower. The innocuous notes were kept on a shelf for collection. The Japanese guards who patrolled the building when there were groups of internees, would sometimes grab a note or two, demanding to know what was in it. To start with one of the interpreters would be sent for to decipher the message. However, as most of them were of no importance they tired of this. Nevertheless Joyce and/or myself had to be extremely cautious when slipping them into a book; hence the busy time of school leaving, with others milling about, was chosen for special messages.

Myra asked one evening if I could take her class the next day as she had a very uncertain tummy. She drew me a plan of who sat where, with their names. There were only nine of them, and she warned that Billy, the towhead in the front line was the rabble-rouser, but could easily be conned into being on your side!

I took my place, waiting for the gang. Myra had apparently told Billy that there was to be a stand-in for the next few days. The curriculum for the hour didn't look too fearsome. The gang filed in, taking their places, putting down their stools. When all were settled I called out my good morning. There was no reply, but Billy's hand shot up.

'Yes Billy, what is it?'

'Fuck off!'

This was so unexpected that I burst out laughing, and was convulsed for a couple of minutes. When I was able to control myself, Billy was still standing, the rest staring at me belligerently! Now for the attack to restore order.

'OK Billy, would you all like me to fuck off and you take the class or will you fuck off and let me take the class?'

There ws a very brief stunned silence, and then everyone was convulsed with the giggles. Billy sat down, slightly pink in the face, but subdued, and the class continued. The hour was spent with questions and answers, mostly to do with how long I would be in charge. I got around that one by saying happily not too long, and Billy was on my side! The children were particularly noisy, and the class delayed. The group to follow was shuffling about. Joyce came to open the library. I saw one of the special couriers slide his hand over the counter, and to my alarm a couple of Bandy-Bastards clomped in officiously. Hurriedly the gang and I made for the door, and the kids took off, whooping round the building.. To my intense relief the nosy guards followed us out, and watched the antics of the gang. Billy appointed himself as my personal aide, and calling out to the others, 'Cm'on, small fry', we marched out of the area.

My second session was all sweetness and light, Billy presenting me with a rather crumpled fag he had no doubt got from Humpty Dumpty! Thus peacefully ended my efforts at school-mistressing.

Signs of the first typhoon were building up, with a curiously heavy yellow sky, but no suggestion of the roaring winds to follow. Junks and sampans were knifing through the seas to their shelter in the bay. Then came the onslaught of torrential rain. There was virtually no defence against the storm. The winds reached a frightening gale force. Only the most necessary outside movement was tackled.

No cooked meals were possible that day. The kitchens awash, rations unable to get through. The logs of firewood stored in the kitchens tossed about like small canoes in the swirling waters of flooded drains and angry river roads. Waterfalls cascaded down the hillsides carrying branches, stones and mud.

Camp was battened down as safely as was possible, the ground floors taking the brunt of the water forcing in under doors. Windows were broken, possessions piled up as space allowed in the corridors away from the open. The day slushed on. The sky, when visible through downpours of heavy rain, was a livid bruise. The fury of the thunder joined in the cacophony of hurtling debris, lit up by wondrous displays of sheet and fork lightning. Roof tiles, branches, uprooted branches and broken glass were being bounced and blown around the camp. Most of us had been through many typhoons, all carefully prepared for, but this was awesome. We wondered now how our men were doing across the harbour. Their buildings were certainly not as well constructed as ours. And what about the poor Chinese citizens, how were they faring? Later we heard with sorrow that there had been many serious injuries and deaths amongst the Chinese population from the brute force of the 1942 typhoon.

By the time the eye had passed over the Island and the howling winds had quietened, the camp was limp with exhaustion. We knew there would be at least two more days of downpours, but the waterlogged buildings and blocked drains had to be cleared as quickly as possible. At least the weather was hot. As we began to lick our wounds it was refreshing to feel the rain; all hands worked to clear their areas.

There were some casualties: cuts from broken glass, twisted ankles, a few fractured limbs to workers slipping and tripping over hidden objects in the water-swollen gullies – the final indignity being the eruption of the sewage tank! This called for immediate repairs, not an enviable task, interrupted by a most unpopular character in our hierarchy, known as 'Willy Wet-Legs'. He wandered up to inspect the progress, keeing a good distance from the offensive piece of repair work, shouting inadequately, 'Nice work, chaps, keep going! Splendid, splendid!' His encouragement was not appreciated, which he realised when one of the disgusted men yelled, 'Piss off behind your desk and pick your bleeding nose!'

One of the most serious losses to the camp were all the tenderly cared for allotments growing vegetables. Dr Herclots was a world authority on plants and had a well-nurtured area of tomatoes, pak choy, choi sum and many other easy-to-grow greens. Now there would be nothing left. The gardeners, however, were an optimistic brand of people and after the obvious grouses they were busy planning the next season's delicacies. Meals, particularly for the sick, were going to be pretty difficult to make healthy and palatable. Our good friends, the Stanley fishing fleet, would still smuggle in the odd banana to keep the kids happy! The Stanley market had always been famous for its variety of edibles; after all they had a great fishing fleet to cater for.

I met Suki during my turn as 'gunga-din' for the room. We were almost permanently on water rationing, for one reason or another. Suki was small, not very pretty but with a beautiful skin and thick black hair. She was Japanese. We chatted away, and I was naturally curious as to how she had landed up in the camp. Suki told me that her husband was a British merchant seaman, and on December 6, 1941 he had been recalled to his ship whilst on a few days' leave. She was a very withdrawn soul, and obviously felt lonely and an outcast. The Japanese despised her for marrying one of the inferior race, and the Chinese women in camp, wives of British subjects, despised her for being a Japanese, quite certain that she had been infiltrated to spy on us.

I was interested in her story, and we arranged to meet later in the day, Suki was painfully grateful for any sign of friendship. We met often, sometimes pooling our rations, and sitting in the quiet of the cemetery, overlooking the endless changing moods of the sea, while she prayed her Jimmy was safe. Her father had a fish stall near the Tokyo fish market, and in their back garden her mother supplemented their diet by growing vegetables, the despised taro being the most prolific!

She thought she must have been about five or six years old when the great earthquake struck. Suki remembered a very small baby she was allowed to hold on her lap, and two or three older children around. She also had a picture of running down a road, with people frantically rushing about, buildings, stalls and homes collapsing, but in front of her was a rickshaw speeding along empty. Someone beside her seemed to disappear into the road. Then she watched the rickshaw slowly topple sideways, and she could only the shafts sticking up. Terrible noises were erupting, thick hot dust swirling everywhere. Nothing more. Her next recollection was of lying on the floor in a room full of people, in funny dresses. An eternity passed. She was bathed, fed. One leg was immovable, but most terrifying of all, there were no familiar faces. Suki remembers crying a lot, calling for her mother. People used to come into the room, which she began to realise was full of other children, peer at them, shake their heads and cry. There was a very kind lady who came to talk to her every day, and bring her sweeties. One day she was helped up to walk; one leg was very stiff and hurt. Her bewilderment grew but she couldn't understand what the kind lady was trying to tell her.

One day the kind lady took her away from the room, and writing on a lot of papers she left what seemed a very large building. The home she went to was much grander than the one she remembered. Again there were two older boys and a very happy smiling man. She grew up as their own. Her adopted parents had a tempura bar in a road she didn't recognise, but this became her family. As she became older the kind lady, whom she now knew as Mama-san, explained to her how she came to be adopted. She loved them all very much. Even so, memories surfaced once in a while. She was always afraid of crowds, and most particularly of rickshaws. When she was fourteen she went to help her father and two brothers in the tempura bar, if they were very busy. She was mostly in the small kitchen behind, getting the dishes of fish and dried seaweed sorted out to serve. Suki had been to school and could read and write fairly fluently. She mostly loved to paint the pine trees and mountains where the family sometimes went for a brief holiday.

Business became good, and Papa got larger premises so that he could have a few tables for patrons to sit round and have a simple meal. The family had a lot of friends who were in and out of the restaurant quite regularly. The patrons were mostly Japanese, but now and then a foreigner would come in for a meal. They were mostly seamen. One young man, who spoke Japanese with great ease, came very often when his ship was in port. He too was fond of painting, and inevitably their friendship became close and tender. Her family strongly disapproved. She was forbidden to help in the restaurant, and finally sent to relations in the country. Suki was sixteen at this point, and very much in love with Jimmy, who persisted in seeing her whenever he could.

In the end the marriage was allowed. Jimmy had spent the year courting her. To the family the whole arrangement was a disaster, but Suki understood in her heart that because she was not a true daughter, the unholy alliance was not such a dreadful disgrace.

Jimmy, too, knew the circumstances, and decided that he must take her to Hong Kong, where his ship spent the longest periods. She almost lost her nerve, but the wonderment of belonging to Jimmy surpassed the break with tradition and the family.

So it was that this sad little soul found herself thrust among this strange band of people. Her own, in the bestiality of war, were completely alien to her.

Peg, Myra, Joyce all rallied round to make her feel part of our community. Her English was pretty good, and we persuaded her to help in the maternity ward of the hospital, as she was devoted to young children. There was a bond between us, a completely different way of life, separated from most of our families.

Water conservation was carefully worked out by each group of rooms, or one flat as it had originally been. Our flat consisted of five rooms: one full bathroom with tub, shower, basin and loo, with a separate loo down the corridor. The kitchen was used for storage of the next day's share of vegetable cutting. The amah's room was occupied by Tim, his wife and small boy, with another loo.

The tub was kept as a reservoir, the water being rationed strictly per person. As soon as the tub was emptied, Sanitary-Duty-Wallah had to clean it out, and before refilling, if the water happened to be running, turns were allotted to two at a time for a very quick and short shower; the door was never allowed to be locked as the basin and loo were in constant use. Embarrassment if disturbed under the shower was quickly overcome, as the queue formed for 'Next two, please!' Nan and I usually went in together, Nan chanting 'SPC' whilst the often slightly murky water spurted over us. After many moons of this chanting I asked Nan what the letters stood for. She was a quiet little person, not much given to the protective language, so it was startling to learn that it only meant 'Shit, Piss and Corruption' to the enemy! During the cold months there was no time to chant. In any case the rattling of the teeth prevented any known sound to explode!

# 7

Another New Year. A strongly worded petition had been handed to Colonel Tanaka asking that internees be allowed to use the beach below the jail for health and recreation. To our intense excitement, after lengthy details had been worked out, the suggestion was accepted. What absolute bliss. We were to go in batches, each for a certain duration. Two guards would be detailed for beach duty; there was one pillbox on the left facing the sea. Two other guards would shepherd us along the path and down the steps to the actual beach. There was a beach hut at the top of the path, where a further guard was posted. Almost in the middle of the beach, a mile or so out to sea, was a very enticing little green island, not much bigger than a small field. A dire warning was given of what would happen to anyone who attempted to swim to this tempting piece of land. It must have been obvious to the Bandy-Bastards that no one had the stamina to even think upon it. Except, of course, for a few fat and sassy black marketeers, to whom it would be of no interest.

Our group's first trip down was very comical. The assortment of bathing garments ranged from coveralls, a good way to wash them, to what, I am sure, was the prototype bikini! Even our draconian guards were hard put to keep straight faces! They were two forbidding-looking characters, but the fleeting hand-to-mouth, covering their mirth, seemed to dispel their menace.

That first dreamy feeling of the clean, clear, quiet, translucent water sent our spirits soaring. Always ready to take advantage as far as possible of a situation, we slowly managed to get our parties together with as many friends as possible. When it was obvious to the great Tanaka that his brilliant idea had such a calming effect on his charges, the guards were gradually relaxed, one on the beach, one at the hut, one at the start of the long walk to the steps. We noticed flashes of light from the garrison which towered above the beach. These turned out to be some of the licentious soldiery having a look at this peculiar sight. I am quite sure none of the bikini-clad maidens roused any feelings of desire – too many bones and angles!

Each batch got things down to a fine art. The men would carry down buckets, while we of the gentler sex brought whatever containers we could rustle up, to be taken back full of clean blue sea. Slightly up from the right hand side of the beach, looking out to sea, amongst some large rocks, was a lovely pool, with a small waterfall gushing into it. The kids, under the eagle eye of a mum or chum, loved to play there, sailing little boats scooped out of a piece of bamboo or made of leaves.

There was only one tragedy at the pool in those peaceful interludes. A small boy of four was missed during countdown and a frantic search was launched. The guard was beside himself with grief as he carried down the small figure he had found in the pool. Artificial respiration was tried, but the little fellow

116

was dead. Unfortunately his mother was not at the beach, and the person in charge of the pool activities had faithfully marshalled them out for the homeward trek. No one was ever able to figure out how the youngster had escaped his party. Perhaps he had gone back for his boat, or another dip. The poor soul who had been looking after the toddlers at the pool was hysterical, and was taken to hospital, where the doctor was able to give her a sedative.

This naturally cast a terrible pall of gloom over the entire camp. Orders were given immediately that absolutely NO ONE was to be allowed in the pool; it was off-limits. However, as time rolled on, this, like quite a few orders, was allowed to slide. Mostly only adults made use of the pool if the guard was nodding in the pillbox, out of sight.

Then it was noticed that Pillbox Noddy had been replaced by an officious creature, who liked to stand on the roof of the pillbox, gazing majestically over his charges for short periods. Our bamboo wireless at work again relayed that Pillbox Noddy had been severely reprimanded, in fact had been physically beaten before being executed. There was more than a twinge of sympathy for him, especially from those who had witnessed his genuine grief at the death of young Sammy.

Air activity was still fairly sporadic, pundits agreeing that they were most likely recce planes. One morning, luxuriating in the sea, we heard the rat-tat-tat of what we presumed was machine-gun fire, and the angry buzz of what sounded like fighter planes. As there was daily movement up and down the main coast road to the garrison, usually heavy trucks, or frequently lines of marching soldiery, it would be reasonable for some hit-and-run tactics from the

117

mainland. No one paid particular attention as the sounds were fairly distant. However, there was a current of apprehension after the last bombing, and most of the men went quietly down to the waterline, suggesting that people came ashore in case we had to take cover. Almost immediately there was an angry stutter of ack-ack. As we swam into our depth to scramble up the beach we saw the planes literally swooping over the garrison, firing. One guard, Buck-Teeth, couldn't wait to dive into the pillbox as one cheeky pilot buzzed the beach, letting off a few rounds harmlessly across the little Island, as if to give us hope that they would be back.

We returned to quarters at the double, with no more beach parties for that day. The speculation was that the group of fighters were the Flying Tigers, operating out of Chungking, the nearest fully operational base. Weichow was where the escapees made for as it was held by the Nationalists, and had a small landing field and was only about seventy miles away. The evening bulletin did not bother to mention the 'incident', whereas they had given enormous prominence to the 'bombing by our allies, resulting in the murder of internees'. All the blocks were bursting with joy at the first real sight of our own attackers. Suki and myself braved sliding down the short slope to the Indian quarters between patrols, to join Peg and Joyce for the ever-ready celebratory mug of tea. Getting back to our own block was less easy as we had to skirt round the back of Peg's building to the darkest part of the upwards slope, which happened to be higher than the side we slid down. Emerging behind one of the blocks, across the road from our own sector, we were hidden until the final sprint. We arrived back somewhat breathless with exertion and the ever lurking fear that we would be spotted. However, as it was not the first time we had made the trip, the going was easier. Peg and Joyce knew our approximate timing, and if happily there was no shouting from our side went thankfully to bed!

One or two unlucky internees had been caught out of quarters after hours, and were subjected to most unpleasant punishment. One had actually been jailed for several weeks, as the Japanese suspected his purpose was other than a romantic meeting. For some time after that most of us stayed close to home.

The library was one of the hotbeds of rumour and gossip. This was natural as it served the whole community, so that items of interest or drama were imparted and discussed round the bar. On rainy days our colleagues tended to linger. One wet morning a borrower from the bungalow area, came in damp and flushed with excitement, and we all heard her incredible tale.

Apparently the night before, Mick and Linda, who were romancing together, had been chatting in the garden, close to the bungalow, to allow a hasty retreat back inside should a guard be spotted. Some little time passed when they heard soft padding and snuffling moving towards their rendezvous. The warning was taken and they left for the safety of indoors.

The next morning, when the bungalow occupants were outside for roll-call, unmistakeable large paw marks were discovered in the garden round the side of the bungalow where Mick and Linda had been. The imprints certainly of an animal very much larger than a dog. None of us really believed this absurd piece of news, and decided someone was trying to enliven a dreary wet day.

For several days these paw marks were seen around the various bungalows. A watch was kept. Finally it appeared that at least two of the watchers had definitely seen a very large beast. They both insisted that it was a TIGER. Now the whole camp was astir with drama. A report was made to Japanese HQ, who immediately dismissed the whole affair as the product of hallucinations, a cowardly attempt to panic the camp. Nevertheless extra guards would be mounted to verify the report.

Sure enough the beast, searching for food, roamed its way Up-The-Hill to the kitchens of Jap HQ. The Japanese in residence actually saw the tiger before it had taken fright and loped off to its lair, wherever that was. The mighty Tanaka could not fault his own men. A shoot was arranged, with a posse of our men to act as beaters.

The news spread amongst the villagers, who confirmed that before the hostilities had commenced, there had been a small Chinese circus in Kowloon. Most of the animals had been slaughtered, but it was quite possible that in the confusion, one or two of the unfortunate creatures had got away and taken to the hills. It was also possible, if there was indeed a tiger, that the beast had swum over to Hong Kong Island and hidden up in the remoter areas, living off the barking deer which inhabited the secluded parts around Stanley and Shek-O. These charming little creatures were protected game and often wandered down into the gardens of the big houses at night, to strip them of the greens. It was well known that the Japanese, and the villagers if they could, had killed quite a few for their flesh. No doubt the rifle shots of the Japanese had flushed the tiger from that isolated part of the Peninsula to forage for food closer in to the camp area. He was, after all, familiar with the scent of man. The whole camp was agog. This was certainly a bizarre turn of events. The plans were drawn for the beat. As the animal was invading the camp, the hide-out must be reasonably close in the vicinity of the camp. It was decided that the hills rising above and to the right of the beach, where there was thick undergrowth, were the most likely places for cover.

The posse were geared for action, long bamboo poles, and the clanging of tins. Those of us who were able to, scrambled for an advantageous spot from which to view the spectacle. The children were wild with excitement, but the older and wiser souls were sceptical of the whole story – just another ruse to stir up trouble.

The first day was unsuccessful, and the men came back hot, wet and almost on their knees. The sceptics had a told-you-so look, but the believers were sure that the next beat would drive out the quarry.

Among our men there was a crackshot marksman, with many years of experience of always hitting the target smack on. Somehow Tanaka was persuaded to allow this man to be in front for the kill. The next day a different area was beaten. Closer to the camp. The noise, louder than the day before, was clearly heard. An atmosphere of tension pervaded. The prisoners in jail must have indeed wondered if the demons of hell were on the rampage. As the day wore on there was a universal unspoken fear that during the heat of the chase some trigger-happy guard might fire, perhaps wounding one of our beaters.

Shouts could be heard of the sighting of the beast, and then a single shot echoed round the hills and bounced off the prison and block walls. The marksman had got his target. Shortly speculation would end and word would reach us that the mighty hunter had been successful.

The beaters returned exhilarated by their two-day break from routine. The road and hillside across from it were lined to watch the triumphal procession of a poor, skinny moth-eaten tiger, swinging from a bamboo pole, being carried out of camp. The main exit was crowded with the local villagers gawping and clapping the exit of the tiger. The brief safari had ended, but the tale of the tiger was a fresh subject of conversation. One of the comics in the Indian quarters kitchen suggested that we might get a sliver of meat in the next stew pot!

News was being smuggled in of the brutality being meted out to the POWs, and of the terrible hardships suffered by the local population. As many as possible were being herded from the Island and Kowloon into the mainland, as supplies became more difficult. Several hundreds of fisherfolk were sailing off in their junks for Wei Chow, and less troubled fishing grounds.

Miyake, the interpreter, had told a confidant of his on our committee, that there was much disquiet amongst his masters. Food for the populace was scant, the small amounts of cultivation destroyed during the fighting, then by the typhoon. There was fear, unrest, and lack of co-operation by the people. The gradual loss of the fishing fleet was sorely felt, harsh punishment driving more of them away from their harbours. Government food stores were looted. There was a stubborn resistance to rule by terror. This indeed was a great way of encouraging Co-Prosperity for East Asia. Victories on the two battle fronts, Europe and the Pacific, were eagerly accepted.

We were able to watch the magnificent junks, with their proud tan sails before the wind, from east and west of the Peninsula, praying that Tin Hau, their Goddess, would bless them with a safe voyage. Most of us had witnessed the occasional motor patrol boat chasing a lone junk, firing on it and then setting the junk on fire. This, we learned, was to discourage the fisherfolk from fleeing. The Japanese propaganda machine had obviously been sabotaged, for still the junks sailed away, risking this wanton murder.

Despite news of scanty food supplies, the faithful parcel bearers continued to come once a month, when possible, with their welcome offerings. The ones lucky enough to receive these basic extras were always generous in sharing them with their friends. Twice Mother was given a precious bundle of wrapped tea leaves. Fred's wife, Chantal, had contracted TB and was isolated with the other TB patients in a separate hut that had been selected for these poor souls. Any small amounts of food to be scrounged were pooled for the TB ward.

Medical supplies of drugs were still being smuggled in. Mostly at great risk to the smugglers. Arrangements were carefully made of the time and place these supplies could be found, often outside the wire, buried in the undergrowth near the beach opposite the Indian quarters. The faithful night foragers, Tom and his band of helpers, would take turns at retrieving these bundles. At times they had to be kept hidden for several days in some trusted safe-room until it was considered a no-risk to deliver them to the hospital. The suspected informers were known by Tom's men and a very close watch was mounted on their movements.

Another method was to use the ration lorries but

pay-offs had to be made. Spot checks were carried out. The discovery of smuggled goods meant the drivers and unloading teams being marched off to Gendarmerie HQ to face sentence of jail or even execution. The practice was quickly abandoned as placing the whole camp in jeopardy. There was also the threat of withholding rations for an unspecified period if illegal goods were found.

The Blacks took over the operation of supplying certain of the hospital needs which were not forthcoming through official sources. Our committee guaranteed payment. The Japanese were aware of the practice which was condoned by their rake-off.

Saleable gold trinkets were in short supply. So prices through the Blacks hit a new high. A duck egg fetched £5 whilst a packet of cigarettes cost £10, paid for by guaranteed IOUs.

The first camp wedding was a great event. The couple had in fact been engaged before our internment. All their friends pooled enough ingredients together for the kitchen to bake a delicious one-tier cake. An odd assortment of gifts was collected, the most acceptable being two tablets of precious Red Cross soap! Their happiness was shattered too soon. Alec, the bridegroom, was arrested at ration stations a week or so later for collecting smuggled goods.

Amongst the Indian warders employed by the Japanese in the jail, there were two intensely loyal men. Loyal to their former officers who were in camp. They kept a tally of POWs brought in and of the executions carried out, news of which from time to time they managed to leak into camp.

Several weeks after the arrest of Alec came the tragic news that he had been executed. This horrific message was very close to home. A deep depression hung over us all. It was terrible to see the anguish of his new wife, the third victim of desolation in our midst.

Just as life in our area was slowly returning to the acceptance of normal daily chores, a rather delicate and tricky situation presented itself for the committee to sort out. Two women friends who had been assigned an amah's room, began to show signs of deterioration in their devotion to each other. The younger, and more attractive member of the liaison, was being courted by a kitchen worker. He was most persistent, lavishing kitchen perks to his lady friend. Her companion began to show symptoms of vicious jealousy. Trouble was brewing as she raved around camp, voicing the unfaithfulness loud and clear. The blockhead had the task of trying to re-allocate the guilty party, but no one was willing to change places! A move was forced when the jealous one assaulted her lost friend by biting a chunk out of her bottom. The scar would always be a memory of her infidelity. She was, however, found other accommodation in a different part of camp, with a warning to keep her distance and keep the peace!

Yachi was a bumptious, sadistic NCO. He took a delight in showing up at the least expected moment, either to check on the sentries or poke his porcine nose around quarters. The kitchens in particular came in for strict scrutiny on his rounds. His favourite trick was to barge into a bin of fish heads and tails, or a bucket of vegetables ready to be used for the meals, knocking the contents over the cement floor. Clicking his tongue elaborately, he would stalk off to find an excuse for using his rifle butt. He usually found this excuse amongst the woodcutters, where one or two, sitting down for a smoke, were not on their feet in time to give the salutary bow. Lookouts signalled as soon as he was spotted, the food containers were hastily moved to the back wall, and the woodcutters alerted.

He had not as yet made a foray to the beach. No doubt he didn't want to get his boots full of sand. One morning when there was a hint of rain in the air, and some dark clouds scudding overhead, Tom, Rick and I decided to fill our battered containers from the sea and get back to quarters before the deluge. Getting permission from Pillbox Joe to leave, we started up the steps, quite a feat with three full loads of water. We made the top without slopping too much precious water, and started down the path. On the left were clumps of grass, wet from the dripping bodies of previous homeward bound water carriers.

Looming towards us came Yachi, flanked by two guards. We moved off the path onto the grass and putting down the buckets, stood waiting to give the customary bow. As the trio approached, Yachi well to the fore, he shouted out some unintelligible order, at which his two flunkies kicked two of the buckets over. Yachi then aimed one boot at the third and skidded on the wet surface, landing with a thud on his backside. There were a few stragglers who had arrived at the top of the steps at that moment. The static in the air was palpable. The stragglers retreated in confusion. We were rigid, waiting for the good earth to swallow us! The next few moments passed in silent slow motion. Yachi climbed to his feet, motioned the guards to collect the empty containers, lined them up in front of us and turned carefully on his heel, returning the way he had come.

As they disappeared round the far wall, the breath we let out would have knocked down the walls of

Jericho! We headed back down to the beach on spaghetti legs. Falling into the sand we exploded with great gasps of laughter. Eyes streaming, tummies aching, Rick remarked that it was like a Laurel and Hardy film. He expected Yachi to lumber up, his arse growing grass, and custard on his face! The last laugh was, however, on ourselves. Having left our full water container against the wall whilst we had a refreshing dip, we crawled back up the steps. No sign of any containers. The word was spread around that the CONTAINERS MUST be returned. Much later, when it was too late to revisit the beach, the containers were spotted lined up against the railings opposite Block 4, all empty! It was a rotten trick, but needless to say we did not pursue detection of the culprits.

The sequel, however, was a nuisance campaign. For a time the odd day to the beach would be cancelled. Alternatively, on our way down the rear guard would prod those nearest him for more haste. If it was a really hot brass-rod sun, permission to return to quarters would be delayed long enough to make the beach parties late for the morning meal. We guessed these acts of petty ill-humour were the brainchild of Yachi.

This harassment stopped abruptly several weeks later. Humpty Dumpty's relief, Bugger-Lugs, a rather simple fellow who enjoyed the odd exchange of chit-chat with one of the kitchen staff, who in turn had picked up a bit of Japanese, learned that our gallant Yachi had gone for a brief leave to the big city. Thankfully he didn't return and his replacement was too idle to go on the prowl!

All of us of the female species watched the night sky for signs and portends. A blue moon, a shooting star or a falling star. Any of these could be an omen of glad tidings. No one had ever doubted that we would win the war. The time factor was a matter of guesswork. The non-productive predictions were beginning to dampen our inward thoughts. Only with our very good friends would the possible outcome of the Allies' victory be voiced. The camp mystics would tell fortunes of war with cards. It became a mania to have your cards read ostensibly for fun, but too many souls took this so seriously that it became boring to have to listen to what fate had in store for them! There was no crossing of palms with silver; if available a couple of fags might change hands. Premonitions were bandied around, usually in a dream of being freed. This was all really harmless, and helped to cheer up some unhappy souls.

One calamitous event did not show up in the cards. The Japanese had got the scent of rumours that another escape was being planned. Most likely it was idle speculation and gossip going the rounds. Any hint among ourselves was quickly quashed but not forgotten by Tanaka and his staff. The order was decreed: all the young men without dependants in the camp were to be housed in Stanley Jail each night, with a promise of freedom each morning. This was a fearful blow to us all and called for a hasty countil of war by the committee. The authorities were adamant. The nightly lookout rosters had to be adjusted.

The only male bastion were the police officers and a percentage of the inspectors, who had their own separate quarters. They were to be the spearhead of the jailbirds. At roll-call the blockheads presented their list to the Japanese. That evening the formations were counted and listed. The march to the jail started, the men singing lustily, all the old war marches, and not a few rugger songs, the rest of us cheering wildly, except the men left behind like Rick, who somehow felt they were lepers.

As the main gates were closed on the last group, there was a sudden silence, and nervously glancing at those forbidding portals, we drifted back, gathering in small parties to mull over the implications. That night Rick and I were at our posts when a much disliked and distrusted member of our community joined us. He was in the right bracket, age and fitness wise, to have been 'inside'. With a tentative leer his opening remark was unwise. 'Hallo, hallo, doing a bit of canoodling, eh.'

Rick was a big man, although he had lost a lot of weight, as most of the men had. I turned my back on Stinker, his camp-given nickname. Rick caught him by the shoulder. 'You bastard, what are you doing lurking about, friends at court?'

Stinker shrugged himself free whilst kicking Rick on the shin. He had disappeared round the corner of the corridor in a flash. Rick was after him. Their voices had been raised, and several late sleepers came out to find out the cause of the noise. Assuring them all was well, I asked Flo, from the room across to ours, to hurry and tell Janie, Rick's wife, who was very frail after a virulent bout of flu, that there was nothing to worry about – if she were awake. The sound of scuffling and angry voices stopped, but the bile rose in my throat. Any kind of fracas and the guards would be alerted.

Rick returned, slightly dishevelled, his right fist still bunched, and very red. 'OK – sorry – no bones broken but possibly a spiteful tip-off on lookouts!'

Quiet footsteps came padding round the corner. Not sure what to expect, we both grinned with relief as Phil appeared. 'Christ, Rick, don't rock the boat,

129

that piece of turd could turn nasty.'

'How come you're about?' asked Rick.

'The bad news woke me up to say you had assaulted him on his way for a pee.'

The three of us had a quiet snigger. 'He had a point,' said Phil as he made to return to his room. 'Nice signs of a shiner brewing.'

'What of tomorrow, Rick?' I asked.

'You'll see, the boys will be back, I have a hunch these are scare tactics, but they won't work, morale is still pretty high regardless.'

Next morning, very early, the gates of the jail swung open and out came the boys full of good cheer. It was like a carnival, everyone cheering them and the children prancing alongside as they filed along to their buildings. The cooks came in for a barrage of friendly insults. 'Overslept you idlers,' 'The toast is burnt,' 'How was your midnight feast?'

Back to the day's routine and to learn if they had any news of the other lads who had been taken away. This nightly ceremony continued for a brief spell. The authorities, as they often did, got bored with the whole scheme, especially as it interfered with the mechanics of things in the camp running more or less smoothly.

The doctors, who had rightly been exempted from this new rule, were also anxious as to the state of health of those who had already been sentenced. Wisely no details of any kind were ever passed around. Neither was Stinker in evidence for night roll-calls or nightly visits to the corridors. These night spot checks were one exercise that had been stepped up since the confrontation between Rick and the Stinker, which could have been an offshoot of his suspected collaborating. Curiously this disturbing habit grew suddenly less frequent, until it was finally abandoned altogether.

Our tailor's shop had a bonus of empty flour sacks. Some of the contents had been allocated for the hospital and children, some found its way to the black market. But the empties were in great demand for summer clothes. I was one of the lucky ones in our block to be issued with a pair of shorts, with the message, or what was left of it, 'Best Australian Flour' on one cheek and a bunch of grapes on the other. Also a top which was almost waist length so it could be fastened in front with a knot. To be kept for festive occasions only! Tony suggested stencilling my name across the front – the forerunner of the tee-shirt? We knew this would create a precedent so it was left unadorned. The tailors were working full pressure, getting costumes ready for the first ballet, which certainly produced some very artistic work. Tony's talent in designing the sets with what materials were available helped enormously. He had sketched a number of terribly funny caricatures which it was a great privilege to be allowed to see, as of necessity the ones of the Japanese had to be kept carefully hidden.

Most of the perimeter guards had been replaced by Formosans, by this time. They were much more fearsome than the Japanese. It was advised that contact with them was to be avoided whenever possible. They were like killer dogs straining at the leash for a chance to strike at the slightest excuse. Some of the chaps' 'illegal' activities slowed down until the measure of these monsters could be gauged. News and messages from the outside as well as smuggling were discouraged.

# 8

During the long summer evenings rules for fraternising in our own compounds were relaxed. It was a great relief to be able to stroll in the open without fear of being hunted back indoors early. The sunsets were always spectacular; the moon rose over Snek O in unbelievable beauty. The environment faded for a while and memories, some poignant, crowded out the immediate and ever present thoughts of when and how this unreal existence would end.

Carol had worked hard with the children's dancing classes. They were to stage an afternoon performance on the grassless lawn in front of the club library. There was wild excitement amongst the young, as they presented themselves with the aplomb of professionals under Carol's eagle eye, and their mums' nervousness. Even the old Bully-Boy from Up-The-Hill attended, clapping and laughing with us in all the right places. Billy was a magnificent Robin Hood, although at times we feared he would break into mimicking the guards! All went off splendidly and there were contributions from the audience of tasty morsels in the clubhouse at the end of their finals. The spontaneity of the afternoon had been great fun and the children were all clamouring for their next entertainment to start rehearsals!

Musical talents were encouraged to forget their shyness. Joyce had a lovely light clear voice and one of the doctors a stirring baritone. They were persuaded to sing for us at concerts. There were classical and jazz piano recitals as well as beautiful poetry readings. Chris, who had been attached to the education department, was able somehow to convince the Japanese to allow him to have his gramophone in the camp, with a collection of records, including most of the operas. These were played over and over again. There could never be a surfeit of the pleasure and comfort we had enjoyed when the evening came to an end.

One morning the exciting news was circulated that letters had been received through the Red Cross for a number of internees. The list was not very long, but everyone rejoiced for the happy group who gathered to collect their mail. Friends shared their news with those who had not had mail. Joyce had a letter of love and reassurance from her husband who was in the Navy. Dear little Suki was clutching her as yet unread letter to her wildly beating heart, as she asked Peg and I to share her good fortune. Her Jimmy was alive, well and loved her. Our eyes were moist as we watched Suki in a trance, reading and re-reading her precious news. For the disappointed majority there was hope of yet another chance, perhaps soon.

Even more worth waiting for were letters, which might be allowed, from our men in the POW camps. The Red Cross letters, an unexpected bonus, could be the forerunner. We clung to this fantasy, hounding the people likely to be the first to know that the Japanese would allow an exchange between ourselves and the boys across the harbour.

Wishful thinking prevailed! Some weeks later we

were issued with one postcard each, the orders were!

(1) Twenty-five words to either a member of the family overseas, or to a POW in one or other of the camps.
(2) No mention of any person in our own camp.
(3) No mention of the state of our health!
(4) No questions to be asked.
(5) Words must be printed in block capitals.

This made it rather difficult to fulfil the offer of twenty five words. No question of grumbling, just the idea of contact would be wonderful, especially as the promise was that replies from the POW camps would be allowed. How long before our cards would arrive, how long before we would get the promised reply? More guesswork and speculation to keep us on tenterhooks, to be debated at our evening news sessions!

Postcards were to be handed in the next day to our HQ office, when they would be sorted, delivered Up-The-Hill for censoring, then hopefully be on their way. All over camp people were chewing the ends of their pencils, ruminating on what to write. My first idea was to put down 'Love You' eleven times, leaving two words for the salutation, and one for my name at the end. After giving this endless thought, I decided it looked pretty silly and unimaginative. The postcard was completed, having slept on my final decision:

'Darling heart – miss you, love you. Much water has flowed under the bridge since we last saw each other. Love to you all, Mother, Me.'

That evening was a joyous one, most of us discuss-ing again and again how long before the chaps got our messages, even more important, how long before they would be allowed to reply. Of course our happiness was tinged with a sadness for the many souls who would never get a reply. The full burden of their loss would open up the scars they tried so hard to live with. If indeed we were to get the promised replies, new sorrows too would have to be faced up to. A chilling prospect, which none of us had really dared to voice aloud or dwell upon even in our innermost thoughts.

There was a sense of euphoria now that something tangible had at last happened. For a great many of us there was a delicious feeling of anticipation. Compassion, too, filled our thoughts at the disappointments ahead for many of our friends and others in the camp.

Friday came round again, my morning to join the happy band of taro slicing. It seemed that it was always Friday. How much less irritating if there could be some nice green potato tops to cut up. The four of us were busy taking our quota of the offending ration when Phil arrived trying not to show how disturbed he was. He called out to me, 'Come along to the office for a minute, will you.' Not a question, a command. As Phil hurried me to our Holy of Holies I could feel my tummy dropping down about two floors. Several chums called out, 'On the mat?' 'Don't forget to share the parcel.' Joyce worked in the office; there could be a message for me. When we were inside the room I saw Joyce's white face. She gave a rather wiggly smile, and touched my arm as I passed her.

The President was standing beside his desk, Miyake stiffly on his left. My mouth was as dry as the Arizona Desert. A kaleidoscope of people moved. Phil went out through the door. A precise, rather monotonous voice spoke while Miyake nodded. Through the one-sided conversation, I could hear perfectly well what was being said, but was unable to relate the order given to myself.

That all too familiar smell of fear assaulted my nostrils. The full implication of the President's monologue hit me where my stomach should have been. Captain Miyake was to escort me Up-The-Hill to the Commandant.

Joyce was allowed to accompany me to the foot of the steps. I felt quite numb as Miyake marched me quickly through the door that Phil and I had come through, was it a hundred years ago? I could hear my clogs clapping on the road. The sound was a thunderous roar which threatened to split my skull. I was hazily aware of friendly faces. The King Pin, whom we lesser mortals seldom saw, flashed me a wink and a thumbs-up sign, which made me wince. Mother was standing by the roadside, Phil holding an arm, as she tried to struggle towards me. Miyake shook his head.

At the bottom of the steps was a sly-looking oaf in guards uniform plus bayonet. Joyce touched my arm again, whispering, 'I'll be here'. The oaf fell in behind me. We started at a quick pace up the steps, which I tried to count, but kept missing the last number. There was something stinging the backs of my bare legs, urging me to go faster.

The compound gave the impression of normality, gardens well tended, the tennis courts well used. Pictures of those happy days flashed through my mind. It was hard to believe that had happened in another era. Miyake motioned me to stop. A second oaf came forward, and the two of them flanked me on either side. Miyake went through the guarded door of the Big House. My adrenalin glands began to work overtime. Christ, a flashback to the epitaph, 'Ladies all . . .' Oh, Jesus, not HERE, not NOW. The saliva was fortunately seeping back into my mouth. A staccato of small coughs, my throat was working. The thundering in my ears cleared with a deep swallow. The cobwebs began clearing from my mind. They would need to if I planned to keep it! The faint sound of the sea and the scent of the shrubs had a soothing effect. The sweat clinging to my body, tickling my hair and running down the back of my legs helped to dehydrate my bladder, which suddenly seemed at bursting point. Not the time to raise my arm. Another flashback, this time to young Billy, that very funny morning. 'Fuck you too.'

The room I was led into I remembered by its contours, not by its present contents. What dominated it was Tanaka seated with his back to the French doors, behind a large expanse of cluttered desk. The oafs positioned me between the desk and the main door and stepped back. I made my bow. Miyake stood to the left of Tanaka whose eyes were directed past me, focusing on an object behind. Tanaka barked. Miyake translated the bark.

'Do you know why you are here?'

'No.'

'Reply, "No Commandant Tanaka".'

'No Commandant Tanaka.'

Another bark from Tanaka. Miyake took a large silver box from the edge of the desk, opened it in front of Tanaka, who removed a cigarette which he put between his lips. A lighter flashed. Miyake held it to the cigarette. The ceremony over, Tanaka lumbered out of the chair, still not looking at me, and walked past and behind me.

The room was unnaturally still. The thudding of

my heart must have sounded as though someone was beating a gong. A louder bark. Miyake obliged.

'Turn round.'

My eyes were tightly shut. I turned slowly so as not to lose my balance, imagination sparking off the terrible sight which might confront me.

'Open your eyes.'

Yes, I thought, and Tanaka will give you a big surprise. Loathing myself for being so childish, I forced my eyelids apart.

Facing me slightly above eye level was the mantelpiece. In the centre was propped a postcard inscribed in block capitals. Tanaka touched the card with the lighted end of his cigarette. I froze, it had to be the card meant for . . . Dear God it hadn't gone. The answer to this whole morning's pantomime would now be explained, or would I have to do the explaining?

Tanaka majestically returned to his seat, Miyake following with the postcard, holding it as if it were a lethal weapon ready to shatter the room.

'Turn around.'

This time my eyes, wide open, rivetted on the card held in front of me. Miyake: 'You wish to send this to an officer in Argyle Street camp.' A statement not a question.

'The Commandant wishes to know what the translation of your code means.' This time Tanaka hissed in English, 'Read the message.' The gymnastics with words and phrases began. I was on a tightrope.

'Which bridge has the water flowed under?'

The questions became confusing, as confusing as my incoherent answers. Only one clear prayer was circling the labyrinth of my mind: Please God don't let them send the card. If my explanation is unconvincing they will attack David. The pattern of conversation and questions kept changing. I was rapidly losing the thread of how to present a cliché. There was the sensation of a fly swat regularly stinging my face, legs and arms. The tightrope was wobbling, becoming slippery – not a tightrope, a bridge, but a bridge didn't wobble. Someone shouted at me to get up. Magically the water from under the bridge splashed over my face. It was cool. A maniacal voice kept repeating, 'Which bridge . . .'

Didn't they know there were no bridges in Hong Kong? I was being propelled forward. A chair was chasing round me. Noises in the vague distance. Tramping feet, a door slamming, laughter? The chair was still, but when grabbing it I must have hit my shins. Christ, they were sore. Why was my hair loose, hanging round my neck, irritating me? A logical question.

There was a small room, a wide open window with a beetle on its back on the ledge. Turn him over. A shout, it was difficult to twist my head round. My hair was getting in the way. I saw a loo, undid my shorts, sat. A face made of yellow plasticine peered through the window. Another shout, the face disappeared. A replica this time at the door, grabbing my arm. Got my shorts up, fine. Back to the hateful room with the mantelpiece and the two bully-boys. Tanaka behind his desk smoking. No Miyake. The French windows were open, lovely blue shimmering sea. Voices low but clear, both talking Japanese. One was not a Jap. I recognised the sibilant lilt of Guy, one of our fluent Japanese scholars. Why was he here?

Miyake returned. Tanaka, still not looking at me, gestured to Miyake, who proferred a cigarette. I dared not shake my head, I would lose it. Miyake was translating sentence by careful sentence. Listening very earnestly I couldn't sort it out, until '. . . now you will return.' (Return where, here or there?)

The ceremony of bowing must have been performed. I was escorted out of the room by two oafs, surely not the same two. A sideway flick of my eyes to the mantelpiece. No postcard. Another bow at the front door. God, the cement path was HOT! How had I lost my clogs? Forget it. Get. At the top of the steps up which I had arrived some time (this day?), one oaf preceded me, clambering down jauntily, me a close second. I bungled the descent – slipped, lurched backwards – a fist grabbed my left shoulder, heaved me upright.

There was Joyce as promised, with a big smile on her lovely face. The oaf delivered me, saluted smartly, and trotted up the steps. Joyce hugging me, half carried me across the road. Home. Had I ever imagined thinking of Block 4 as home?

The return of the prodigal daughter! Everyone was beaming. Mother was brewing up a large borrowed jug of cocoa for the gang who popped their heads in to say, 'Happy you're back.' The head chef, Bottom, had my rations ready to reheat. Joyce whispered that she would collect me in the morning to report at our HQ. We were all slurping back the cocoa, giggling rather nervously, when apparently I rolled into my blanket and started to recharge my batteries. Nature is mostly a cruel old bitch, but knows when to anoint the panacea sleep.

The following morning, after a privileged extra basin of washing water, Joyce arrived with a small first aid kit to attend to my 'wounds'. Really very minor. Self-inflicted bump on the back of the head extremely tender and two cut shins where I had obviously bounced off a piece of furniture. A few bruises on the arms and right cheek, but no teeth missing. Of course an extremely lacerated ego!

At the office I was told that a very impatient Tanaka, wasting his time on a stupid female, had resorted to Miyake's advice and appealed to Guy, who was highly respected by the Japanese hierarchy for his knowledge of their customs and language, to shed some light on the suspect sentence. By carefully wording the explanation, pointing out that the sender might just as well have said nothing, the words were blacked out, the 'interview' accepted as satisfactory. The meeting was concluded with a strict warning not to discuss the matter. With which I was only too ready to agree. All this I later learned from Guy — having no recollection of the final decision!

Great news to soothe my ignominious day Up-The-Hill was a very strong rumour which appeared on the bulletin board — the glad tidings that the *Gripsholm* was to come to our shores, this time to repatriate the Canadians. A small number but yet another chance of getting news to our families. Sally was a room-mate of Peg's. We would miss her in our bridge circle and camp activities.

Sally had never considered that her passport would open the gates to liberty. She could only dimly remember her parents, who were in the UK, talking about cousin Joe or Aunt So-and-So in some place with a remote name she had never bothered to follow up! Her parents had taken her out to Shanghai where she was schooled, grew up, took a job with one of the well-known companies. Her mother had died in Shanghai, and her father had subsequently married a charming Chinese widow friend of the family. In July of 1937 she had been evacuated to Hong Kong, with other European staff and families. During the next few years she had lost touch with her father. They had never been very close.

What an exciting adventure into a new life! With no relatives to claim her on either side of the Atlantic the Canadian Government were bound to look after her until she found her feet, or perhaps managed to trace Cousin Joe, etc. We all contributed ideas to wonderful plans for her! She must keep in touch with at least one of us, so that we would know the happy ending. Peg and Sally's bridge partner two rooms away, were to share her few possessions, but there was one garment Sally was determined to wear aboard, her comfortable and warm raincoat. Both Peg and Betty were astounded! Neither of then owned a top coat and Sally was going to the land of the free, where she would be provided with warm clothing. Sally argued that she might need it during chukkers round the deck. A three-way feud was building up. Peg threatened to steal the much-prized article, and hide it until Sally was safely on her way. Betty suggested that she and Peg borrow a penknife and shred it. The whole incident became absurd. Sally developed a thing about the wretched coat, and wore it permanently, day and night. It was terribly funny to see her puffing and panting around the camp, or doing her chores in the blazing sun, sporting the offending garment.

The rest of us kept well aloof from their vendetta, hoping there would be a rapprochement. Of course there was, when Sally realised that what had started out as a silly dispute was spoiling a beautiful friendship. She had the grace to ask them to forgive her for being so stupid. They in turn told her that their threat was just a joke. After much laughter and a few

142

weeps, a toast to THE coat in their evening mugga, sanity was restored. Peg and Betty inherited the coat between them to remember her by!

The date of departure was near enough. Sally still had some luxuries hoarded from her last Red Cross parcel so she decided to have a farewell party. The usual pooling of rations to be jazzed up with what extras could be provided between the seven of us. Tom and Danny promised to cater for the bar.

It was a lovely, clear, still, light evening and there was a festive mood throughout the camp. With the impending departure, back to quarters rule was relaxed for a further hour. Friends were milling about saying their farewells, passing their brief messages, and also partying. Tom had produced his out-of-the-hat bottle of rice wine. We had a hilarious meal, spiked with the wine, and ending up with a delicious taste of fresh fruit. Shared oranges and bananas. From across the block a fellow Canadian appeared, brandishing *his* bottle of rice wine. This one was really potent. As Myra, Suki and I had to negotiate the slope we reluctantly passed up another swig.

People were drifting off to their blocks. Tom suggested that we three from up-the-slope had better be on our way, particularly as I had already had a close brush with the authorities. After sentimental farewells, Tom escorted the three of us by the conventional route, where we mingled with the last of the groups returning from the Indian quarters.

The send-off a couple of days later was almost an anti-climax. We waved and cheered as the ship's boats took them off the beach to the *Gripsholm* on their first leg, homeward bound. Another chapter closed. There was to be an evening of 'community singing' and Betty had written a song especially for tonight, 'We're Going To Sail Away'. It promised to be a roaring success!

The evening was still young and some of us had an attack of home-sickness. I suggested that those of us who wanted to take a chance – maybe a slight one, as people were milling about, and the singing due to start – go up the cemetery and see if we could catch a last glimpse of our old friend, *Gripsholm*. Danny and Suki thought it a fitting close to the hectic day, so off we hurried. There were a few types lingering about. We did a recce – no sign of any guards. The cemetery was empty, we thought, and we sat on the wall looking out to that calm and deceitful beach. No sign, except for distant lights, of the *Gripsholm* and we had decided to return to base when a figure came hurrying down the path between the graves and, grabbing Danny by the shoulder, asked if we had heard anyone amongst the headstones. No, we had not. He became panicky – he had promised to be lookout for a couple of his friends who had come for a quiet evening, knowing most people would be at the Sing-song – and had completely forgotten his lookout role. To his horror two guards appeared to be scouting around close to the cemetery. His romancing friends heard the voices, and joined us. Now we had to decide our return plan.

We heard the two guards talking loudly. This could be very serious. We were out of bounds and the light was fading rapidly. The three men guided us to a corner against the far wall. Danny crept towards the entrance to see how near the guards were. We had one good bit of luck on our side, the fear the Japanese had about the 'foreigner's holes for the dead'. We couldn't possibly make a break for it whilst the

Japanese were so close.

After about ten minutes Danny suggested that we three women go together by the bungalows and wait for the men. I did not know the couple whose friend had come to look for them. Fortunately she lived in one of St Stephen's quarters, so we could lose her. It seemed an age before there was any movement. Suki clutched my hand as we heard a scuffle and a gutteral shout in Japanese. More shouting and a terrible scream of fear and pain. There was nothing we could possibly do except worsen the situation. Suki whispered to me that the guards had parted, but one had caught one of the men – apparently the other two had not been seen. It was a long and frightening wait for, we hoped, Danny. I suddenly thought of the unfriendly colonel's wife. Was she really out to get me? We could hear more guards arriving. The man – it was not Danny – thank God – was being really beaten up. My original suggestion of seeing off the *Gripsholm* had not been a happy one, so I hesitated to make a further suggestion that Suki and I find our own way down the hill, and hope that would leave Danny a better chance on his own.

I had certainly got my friends into a no-go situation. It was all happening so quickly now. Danny appeared. They had caught one of the men. Danny knew him slightly. The three of them had separated, and Jack was the unlucky one. Danny arranged that Suki and I would stay up in St Stephen's for the night; safer than trying to make it back to quarters. He would get back and alert my mother and our blockhead as to our situation – we had great faith that Danny would do just that – so spent a sleepless night praying that all had gone as arranged.

The final scenario was better than hoped for.

Danny carried out his plan. Jack had been beaten up for being out of bounds and given a stern warning with a threat of execution should he default again. Suki and I were very subdued for a couple of days. There was no mention on the bulletin board for any 'incident' on the second visit of the *Gripsholm*.

Friday evenings heralded our back to pre-war weekend with half-day Saturday. Half-day in name, which made it sound more glamorous. Naturally the daily chores could not be abandoned. There was, however, a more carefree attitude throughout the camp. Trips down to the beach were less controlled, and curfew usually extended unless some bloody-minded officer decided we had let the side down. His side. Entertainments had really got into their stride, so that music recitals, bridge games, even quick light revues were organised. Most of the occupants of Up-The-Hill went into town in their staff cars. Tanaka either had his own social gathering to entertain, or also took off for the high-life. It was rumoured that our King Pin and his girlfriend occasionally received a royal command to join Tanaka, either at home or in town. No one ever actually saw any of these events; it was an eternal conversation piece!

The only damper of which the pessimists never failed to remind one, was the fact that a trimmed down roster of guards meant that two or more members of the Gendarmerie would be likely to arrive at one of our innocent functions. Their forbidding glares and weaponry had the effect of making us edgy, especially if they snorted down the back of your neck during a duplicate bridge hand! It was tempting to suggest to our committee that all small children should be let loose to surround them with smiles and bows – this might have strained their

146

reputed love of the young as a national trait. Anyway, no one was brave enough to toss the idea to the majority vote!

When our time limit was up we would gather together in small circles to discuss the evening's pleasures, post-mortem bridge hands and produce what snippets of news or gossip we had gleaned. The romancers returned from their quiet retreats and headed for the roof, which was tacitly regarded as their territory.

Should there have been a recent Red Cross parcel, mugs of tea and a snack were a welcome nightcap. The lookout roster had dwindled to just Saturday night, one couple per X number of blocks. The spot room checks were usually after the return of the off-duty guards truck from one of the communities round the Island coast. The trucks were noisy, as were the passengers being driven to the barracks, so that there was warning if a band of inebriated thugs decided to have some fun. These violations became extremely rare. When reported by our committee a very stiff punishment followed. The Commandant's orders were that only an officer and one thug be allowed to carry out a spot check. Generally no officer could be bothered to tramp round a block shining his torch on a litter of sleeping bodies. Nevertheless, most Saturday nights we remained alerted.

It became easier to huddle together on a landing or a staircase for those far into the night chats, reminiscences and plans for the future which helped us through the purpose of our night watches.

The Saturday night of the attempted murdeg was a chilling experience. The motive had been festering for many months, apparent to those closest to the heart of the matter, which concerned a husband discarded for a lover. This was not an unusual situation, but undesirable in such a confined community. The unspoken rule was that our committee dealt with infractions within the camp. No hint of an offence, however minor, must go beyond the committee, which judged the gravity of the misdemeanour. Murder had been unthinkable; therefore no plans provided for dealing with either the killer or the victim.

The unfortunate cuckold's humiliation finally became unbearable. Most of his friends, and the others in his area, had accepted from the beginning of accommodation allocation, that he and his wife had chosen to live in separate quarters, and assumed it was by mutual arrangement. This was certainly not an isolated case.

Harry and Laura seemed to be on friendly terms, but were hardly ever in each other's company. She was a vivacious woman who took a great interest in all the social aspects of camp life, and was also very ready to volunteer if extra help was needed for any project. Ron, a most useful handy-man, was in constant demand as a mister fix-it, and whilst acting as a stage-hand in one of the early shows, met and was attracted to Laura.

It was natural to see them paired off together. After a considerable period of time Harry's friends began to notice that he started to take an interest in the twosome. Mostly in the form of banter with or about them. Then his attitude changed. He became morose, withdrawn, no longer joining the boys in their nightly chat sessions. On Saturday evenings he would moon about, seemingly looking for Laura.

Harry would often drop into the room Laura shared with three other girls on some futile pretext, to 'have a word' with Laura. These words invariably developed into blistering arguments, ending up with Laura in hysterical tears. One of the girls, a good friend to Laura, finally appealed to Harry's room mates to try and convince him that his behaviour was promoting a dangerous situation. Harry's two closest friends tried to take it in turns to be with him on so-called off-duty periods. It was not pleasant virtually being his shadow, and after a long and patient talk with him they rebelled, leaving him to sort things out for himself.

Things calmed down and Harry returned to his normal habits, genial, one of the boys again, his recent belligerence faded. The tension petered out like a sudden squall. The unpleasant interlude was thankfully banished from the minds of those involved. Except in Harry's mind.

Most of us had no inkling whatsoever of this malovent scenario. There were constant riffs and jealousies which were on the whole regarded benignly. Any major crisis would be dealt with by the committee. Up to now there had been no vital issue demanding rigorous action.

The Saturday evening was cooling off after a truly awesome sunset, the bold reds and golds slashed through the sky like an angry painter's brushwork. The happy noisy pursuits were happening for all to join in. People bustling about, dates being made for a bridge game, or a picnic on the beach on Sunday morning, much earnest chatter as to who would bring what in the way of a treat. Finally the hubbub simmered down, with last mugs of tea to be collected before lights out. Mother, with her Irish blarney, had persuaded her friendly chef to heat up a tin of water which she poured over a fresh spoonful of tealeaves,

149

a great treat Mother managed to produce like the magician out of the hat for most Saturday nights. We both tried to stretch something from our Red Cross parcels too, trying to make them last as long as possible for those Saturdays.

The blocks were quietening down. Only the night birds moved cautiously out of rooms, down the corridors for a last minute news special before bed. In the distance the village noises could be heard, the barking of watch dogs on the junks in the bay, the odd car going Up-The-Hill. Nothing untoward. Most people were sleeping. It was getting late. Janie, Rick and I were perched on the balcony of their shared room, watching the dancing lights of the boats in the bay.

We suddenly heard muffled cries and could just see several shadows cross the road to the block in front, and beyond ours. We were quickly joined by two of the other tenants in the room, who had awoken. Another figure appeared through the door. It was Tony. He motioned us to get away from the balcony. A whispered few words with Rick, and they left together.

Within minutes more people were astir and we could make out two figures hurrying down the road towards the sentry stationed at the main junction. A third figure appeared with a dimmed torch, making his way to the block beyond. We could hear men's voices, subdued but somehow sounding urgent. Completely mystified, we could only suppose a baby was arriving unexpectedly, someone had died or been taken seriously ill.

Word was going round the block that there was trouble brewing. People were waking and contacting other sleepless souls to know what was happening.

Rick and Tony were not back so Ben took charge, reminding people that they should go to their rooms; the disturbance in the block might attract the guards, they would hear what had happened in the morning. They dispersed quietly to their rooms, only too aware of the results should the guards become suspicious and invade the block.

A loud gutteral Japanese voice, obviously issuing orders, floated up to the balcony. Ben decided to have a careful look, and as we crouched below the wall he gave a whispered running commentary:

'Two guards escorting stretcher bearers by torchlight. Entering second opening in the block. Stretcher party coming out with blanket-covered body. Going towards hospital with guards and three of our chaps. Other guard with torch and two of our chaps disappearing down the road – gone.'

We crawled back into the room, conscious of disturbances in the neighbouring blocks.

'It's a rum do,' said Ben. 'I'll keep cavey for Rick.'

Ben was the hearty type. He resembled a soccer ball, beginning to deflate a bit over the lack of home cooking and beer. His conversation was larded with 'spiffing tuck – jolly good show – Bob's your aunt'. He loved to be first with the latest bit of gossip, but he was kind and forever willing to do any extra chore that was necessary. He was devoted to his rather dour wife, an angular woman with sad eyes, not very robust in health.

The others crept back to their beds. Janie and I sat on her cot, waiting. 'No chance of a drink, the thermos is empty.' Janie sounded as shaky as I felt. Ben kept popping his head in the door to croak, 'No sign.' Janie suggested I had better return to my room; should Mother awake and find me missing, she would

151

be in an understandable panic. Curiosity, heavy with foreboding, would have to wait. Inching my way to my bedspace, cold and wide awake, Mother touched me, sighed deeply, and slept.

Someone bumped into my bed. Awakening to the sounds of movement, the room was eerily dim. The sky was a dirty grey, and heavy stair rods of rain bounced against the balcony door to an orchestration of deep thunder. High reedy notes of wind were piercing through the cracks ushering in rivulets of water. We set to, dragging the camp beds out of the reach of the storm, and used up what garments we could to plug the water inlets. All down our side of the block people were lurching into the corridors with precious bedding rolls and bundles to stack in the dry spots. The freak storm had erupted quite suddenly, catching the early morning outdoor workers, now straggling in to take cover. We slid what empty tins we could find onto the balcony, to hold the rain water. Word was passed round that only indoor workers should get to their stations – splendid – no roll-call!

Although the urgency to contact Rick on the events of the night before was attacking me with nervous hiccups, the weather seemed to be an omen to wait for either Rick or Tony to come to me. The morning literally floated by with no let up of the waterworks, or snarling thunder giving way to the sun, lurking way up high by now. The normally busy traffic of bodies crisscrossing the open areas was thinned down to a few strange humps on bare spindly legs, sloshing their way to necessary action stations. These were the long-suffering cooks, who would be making their witches' brew for the ravening multitudes!

It was uncanny that there were no queries, or

152

apparent awareness in the block of any unusual happening during the night. As I padded off to my vegetable duty, hoping I might see either Rick or Tony, Janie was leaning against her door. She joined me and as we picked our way over the bundles, asked me to meet her later on the first landing if it was still pissing down; otherwise at the railings overlooking the jail in front of my room. She looked sick and scared as she told me that Rick and Tony had left early with Phil, for the President's office. Attempting a smile of assurance, she returned to her room.

The rendezvous on the landing was to be at two o'clock. Having waited restlessly for about twenty minutes, I realised Janie would not be coming. So borrowing the communal rain cape from the room, I became another hump on bare-footed legs, taking the shortest route to the library for sanctuary, and the company of those who would have braved the deluge.

A cheerful sodden group were gathered round the book-bar. Joyce and I were ready for business. The chatter revolved round the even soggier morning meal, slippery paths, leaking roofs and the glorious absence of guards snooping about on their bandy legs. Jan, one of the Dutch lads in the bridge circle, stocky, a ready grin, wary blue eyes, his short cropped blond hair sprouting with blobs of rain, gave Joyce a note for Tom. He seemed anxious to stay and talk, and as an overture gave us each a small rice biscuit which, he said shyly, he had made himself. His wary eyes flicked towards the door as each drenched newcomer joined us. Soon the groups trailed off, as did Jan. We shut shop, and Joyce suggested I go back with her for the hot drink her mother would have on the hob. Joyce and her mother had been allotted a small amah's quarter with a back area for washing and cooking, and a benjo – Indian-style lavatory. Originally there had been a woman sharing this tiny accommodation. She was a very sick person, being incontinent, which was sad for her, but insanitary for her two companions. This poor woman was soon moved into hospital as she was incapable of looking after herself. She died quite early on in our first year of camp.

On our way down to the welcome hot drink, Joyce said quietly, 'Rick and Janie are with Mother. Rick decided that it would be far safer to explain last night's events privately, as with this filthy rain it would be impossible to meet in a secluded spot on the hillside.'

'You know, of course, what happened, being in the office.' I said.

'Yes,' Joyce replied quietly.

We slithered on in silence, the borrowed rain cape helping at least to keep our heads moderately dry. The sky was still filled with dark clouds gushing out continuous troughs of water, which by now had turned most of the flat land into murky muddy lakes. Many of the quarters had small lights glowing bravely.

Having shaken ourselves loose of most of the wet at the entrance, it was a relief to see Mama-T, Rick and Janie, a short but rather fat smug candle burning, and a warm welcome fug greeting us. After our hallos, and a quick wipe down with a 'good-morning' issue towel, the hot drinks were handed out. Mama-T made a delicious concoction of condensed milk, a good dollop of closely rationed rice wine, and hot water. Nectar!

Warmed and relaxed at last, Rick asked that we please hear him out, before any questions. He

154

explained that Joyce could fill in the official details. He also emphasised that the story must be forgotten in this room, and remain between the five of us. The others concerned had been given the same instructions.

The night before Harry had been with his gang, swapping pre-war experiences. Unfortunately one of the boys had produced a couple of bottles of fairly potent home-brewed wine which had added to their bawdiness. They were grouped near the barbed wire fence dividing the Indian quarters from the lovely beach overlooking Stanley fishing harbour. Passers-by stopped for a few words on their way back to their rooms. Curfew was very near when Pat, one of the few teenagers, joined the gang, telling them that a couple of the 'demolition squad' were prowling around, he thought he had better warn them. Harry became truculent, announcing loudly and belligerently how he would deal with any interference. The gang decided it was time to break up the evening session and make for home. Harry was eventually persuaded to cut out his loud-mouthed bragging, and beat it with the rest of them.

Sometime during the night Lex, one of Harry's room-mates, a tall, wiry, grey-haired man, who had been keeping an eye on Harry and was able to control him up to a point, awoke. The lights from the fishing boats ballet dancing on the now calm sea, threw a dim reflection onto the building. The junk dogs were still barking, ceaselessly keeping away the devils. Lex went to their door for a quick smoke. The sky was festooned with stars. Lex was suddenly aware that a bed space was empty. Christ, it was Harry's.

By this time Harry had managed to inch his way up the slope behind the American quarters, the block across the road facing our block. Harry knew Ron was billeted on the ground floor, which was easy to get into. Lying still to listen for any movement and hearing none, he crawled into Ron's room. He called Ron's name in a loud whisper, not knowing which was Ron's bed space, urging him to come outside for a minute. Ron was instantly awake. He grabbed hold of Harry, telling him to bugger off and keep it till morning. The others began stirring, muttering shut up and piss off, not fully conscious of what was going on. There were louder, harsh voices. The window darkened as another figure crawled through. A frantic scuffle sent one of the figures sprawling onto Ron's neighbour. The other two people appeared locked together, weaving in the confined space, banging against the wall nearest the window. By this time the whole room was alerted. As soon as Ron's companion had disentangled himself from the sprawling figure he realised it was Ron. 'What the bloody hell goes on?' someone growled switching on a shielded torch. Lex was holding a limp, unconscious Harry, whom he had knocked out with a blow to his jaw. Ron was lying on the floor, curled up, arms wrapped around his ribs and blood oozing alarmingly from his mouth. Lex took charge of the unnerving situation. He sent two of the men to get permission from the nearest sentry to take an emergency patient to the hospital, the third man to get hold of their blockhead while he gently lifted Ron, as he was, onto his bed, wrapping what blankets he could round him. He managed to drop Harry out of the window into the darkness.

This was when Tony had come into Rick's room and taken him out. Firstly, to tell Phil there was something very odd going on across the road, and perhaps they could help without arousing too many people. Secondly, it might be as well if Phil could see if Guy, our Japanese scholar, would be willing to be on hand. Tony felt Guy's presence was imperative. Tony did not give any reasons for his suggestions.

Tanaka, apparently, was whoring around in town for the weekend. His deputy was completely bewildered when the sentry appealed to him to hear what Guy had to report. Phil and Guy had gone Up-The-Hill with the sentry, while the blockhead for Ron's quarters had hurried down to the hospital to get a stretcher and the doctor on duty. Tony and Rick went over to Ron's room to offer their help.

The deputy, obviously fearful of carrying the can for any violation of rules in Tanaka's absence, listened to Guy with a certain amount of relief that this was a purely internal matter, a medical emergency of one of the men haemorrhaging from a perforated ulcer. He must be moved to the hospital with all speed, Dr Stuart would probably have to operate. Two extra guards were ordered to accompany the deputy to oversee the man being taken to hospital, and he, the deputy, would talk to the doctor.

Everything was carried out with military precision, and gallant Dr Stuart, having examined the patient, stuck his neck out for the execution sword by assuring the deputy that he must indeed operate, so extra lighting was needed in the theatre.

When the explosive situation had finally diffused, Lex, with the help of Tony, somehow managed to get the now stirring Harry back down the slope to their room. The elements were on their side, as the sky was giving ominous rumbles, and a steady shower a certain amount of cover. It was wisely decided that Tony stay there for what was left of the night, or by now early morning.

A conference was arranged in the President's office as early as possible on Sunday. Present were the deputy, Miyake, Guy, Dr Stuart and all those who had been involved with the 'arranging' for the patient's admission to hospital. There would be an enquiry as to why this seriously sick man had not been attended to before. 'Ye gods,' said Rick, cool heads and fast talking would have to convince the deputy that he had indeed done his duty in saving this man's life. There was a long rehearsal until they were all word perfect before the official conference. Dr Stuart impressed upon them that the Japanese must be dissuaded from examining the patient. Ron, he said grimly, had been viciously stabbed, the knife point puncturing his left lung. He did not want to know any details of how this had happened, but was prepared to send one of his trusted nurses to keep the attacker under sedation for a couple of days, with his much needed and slowly dwindling drugs. At all costs NO indication of what had occurred must be allowed to leak out.

The conference had lasted through most of Sunday, until the Japanese had been convinced that he had heard the solemn truth. The 'item', as he referred to the previous night's emergency, would be entered in his report to the Commandant, when it would be out of his hands.

The nurse had quietly slipped into Harry's room with the injection as ordered by Dr Stuart. Lex promised to be responsible for Harry until it could be decided how to deal with him. Our own police commissioner was given a full appreciation of the whole affair, but naturally the police could not be brought openly into what was reported as a serious medical condition – perforation of an ulcer.

The tragic sequel was not known during that day of continuous rain, which as Rick said, was on our side, keeping movements down to the minimum. During the afternoon Laura had been hurried away to the hospital too. Poor unhappy Laura, so gay and friendly, had a miscarriage. She repeatedly asked for Ron. Suki told her gently that the hospital was very full and busy, and it was a dreadful day to have visitors. Suki had no idea then that Ron was fighting for his life with Dr Stuart and the nurses working tirelessly to help him.

Ron lived, recuperating slowly with Laura's constant attendance. She was not convinced of the ruptured ulcer diagnosis, but obviously afraid to ask what had really happened to him. The doctor stated firmly that on no account was Laura to be told the facts. He also made Laura promise never to tell Ron of her miscarriage. There was no doubt that Laura must have eventually guessed, up to a point, the reason for Ron's condition.

Harry was in room custody. Lex had an exhausting two months looking after Harry, who had become a manic depressive, refused to eat for days at a time, would not talk or have anyone near him except Lex. Very much against his will, the doctor, realising the tremendous strain on Lex, which could not be sustained for an unlimited period, agreed to admit Harry into hospital. His reluctance was in no way deliberately inhumane, it was a matter of space. With the hospital constantly full all the staff and volunteers worked long and arduous hours.

'Rainy Sunday' was a day best forgotten by quite a number of us. No one ever spoke, even amongst ourselves, of the near skeleton in the camp's cupboard. To our credit nintey nine percent of us were good guys and only a minority of one were sons of bitches.

# 9

One of the most universally loved characters was Lou Alcock, satisfyingly nicknamed Baldy-Balls-Up. He had the physique of a Viking and the heart of a lion. His hair was thick and pale gold, as was his luxuriant moustache, which curled at the corners of his wide, mostly smiling mouth. By mischance his teeth were badly spaced: three large white Moses tablets upper front, two lower middle front, but sufficient molars to bolster up the remaining jaw line.

He was a devotee of malaprops, puns and shaggy dog stories. His abominations were 'those fornicating banjo-squatters' (the Indian style lavatory), 'those black running buggers' (the Black Marketeers) and 'those mealy-mouthed Bible thumpers' (our share of missionaries) in that order. At meal-queue time his voice could be heard over a vast distance, calling the hungry to feed on either 'a most *palatable* culinary masterpiece' or 'a *deecilious* gut-rot'. His shy, dark little girlfriend had long since given up squirming and blushing over his murder of the English language, content to enjoy his love and ours for him.

The only male matching his physique was the King Pin's deputy, a much fleshier caricature by dint of his role in the Blacks. Old Baldy-Balls-Up had a penchant for needling the deputy should they be within hissing distance. The deputy's orders were clearly to execute a rearguard action whenever possible.

For some little time there had been a aura of unease amongst the lower echelon in the Blacks. Garbled stories were circulating through the bamboo-wireless that the King Pin's authority was being challenged by his deputy. Unthinkable, as they needed each other, the King Pin for his financial expertise and liaison with the suppliers, the deputy for his control, distribution to the ranks and knowledge of the Chinese language. Mei was our source of meagre information. She was the Chinese wife of one of the many outlets for collecting the bits of jewellery to be sold, a rather square, bright-eyed person, with a very generous heart. She could root out a genuine need for help from stray hints, which she would quietly investigate. If a couple of duck eggs, some extra rice or wong tong would help over a few weeks, through Mei, they found their way – no questions, no IOUs and no thanks.

Now it was Mei letting small hints fall about the suspected coup. Most of the Blacks' regular customers threaded the worn path to their favourite grocer, fearing that in the event of a takeover bid, supplies would be cut off until ownership had been rightfully sorted out. We impecunious peasants gloated over the remains of our Red Cross parcels, and awaited the final act.

The whispers and furtive looks amid much tooing and froing around the King Pin's domain promised early results. The comparatively short manoeuvering for position had been brought to a head by the dastardly hijacking of a supply of cigarettes invoiced for immediate sale. A cutback for the eyes-shut brigade.

By the time the leak seeped down to most of us the magnitude of the daring crime left us aghast. The Blacks were in conference most of the day. This confrontation could alter the life of the camp. We scurried about like frightened mice, trying to find out whether a decision had been reached. The deputy was slated as the cigarette thief in our book. However, the wiser ones guessed at what would be the answer in the power struggle leading up to the hijacking. In fact it was this guess which cancelled the difference of the two top guys and cemented the clan together more closely. Baldy-Balls-Up had obviously intended to splinter the clan by his bold and dangerous plan. He very nearly succeeded.

Although the camp's ruffled surface simmered down within a couple of days, repercussions were rumbling underground. Old Baldy-Balls-Up continued to call out his patron's menus, but remained close-mouthed on the main topic of the settlement in the affairs of 'those black running buggers'.

After a lot of probing and promises not to divulge her story, Mei explained that the garbled versions of the outcome, which were spreading like a brush fire, had been pieced together for the very good reason that the clan had issued a black-out on the entire subject. She did, however, assure us that a middleman had negotiated the return of the stolen property, less two packets already broached by Baldy's helpers. This was considered 'fair do's' as Ben would put it. Mei stressed the fact that the affection in which Baldy-Balls-Up basked, was his ace in the hole. The King Pin had come out of the disaster area with a certain respect. Baldy was canny enough not to push his luck. Knowing that the truth had been leaked he never once made any reference to his part in the fracas.

There were two momentous lines on the bulletin board:

'Mail – foreign and POW Camps.'

'Allowances.'

Hopes were reaching for the stars on the mail issue. On 'Allowances' our committee would expand through our blockheads. Certain internees had been receiving monies via the Red Cross for some time, but as this had never been referred to officially, the blockheads were besieged by the female population bombarding them with questions.

The evening routine was disrupted. Lively troupes milled about, exchanging theories, whilst the blockheads lined up, awaiting their turn to receive the information we were all clamouring for. The news was to be announced in each community after curfew. That would certainly ensure no illicit visiting took place in out of bounds quarters for that night!

Enthusiasm was high, meagre rations forgotten. Even preparation for the late night tea ceremony was pushed into the background. The youngsters too were infected by the fiesta mood, charging squealing round the nearest guard, hands out for a goody, pushing the small pot-bellied child in front to melt the monster's heart! Even seeing the sadness in the eyes of our friends who knew there would be no letter from a loved one, but rejoicing with the hopefuls only dampened the elation momentarily.

Curfew couldn't come quickly enough tonight and instead of lingering in the compounds, sunset-gazing figures scurried off in their various directions for the exciting news. Shouts from anxious mums rounding up their chicks mingled with Master Billy's 'C'mon small fry, home'!

Phil had very sensibly asked for a member to

represent each room in his zone to meet round the entrance hall of our block. As there were five rooms on our landing we elected to ask one of our senior male citizens to attend as our deputy. The popular choice was Rick, who in turn suggested Ben go along with him in case he forgot any details. They were bundled down the corridor with threats of hideous torture should they fail to report the minutest item. Everywhere was buzzing with the hum of voices, hurrying of feet. Lights were still on in most of the rooms where the mood see-sawed between feverish hope and the ever present niggle of possible disappointment.

Suki came to wish Mother and me luck before returning to her room. She said she had felt so happy and grateful hearing from her Jimmy that she couldn't bear it if we didn't have some message to share with her.

Ben's cheerful call could be heard coming up the stairs. 'Thumbs up chaps, splendiferous walla-walla!'

We herded into the corridor, enough butterflies in our stomachs to swamp the Amazon. A few emotional tears glistened in our eyes as Ben and Rick stopped in the doorway, faces glowing like hallowe'en pumpkins, each holding a piece of paper, a proud pennant above their heads.

'We want hush,' quoted Ben, before the rush of questions. Hush they had, as the sshs dwindled.

'Mail first,' an anxious voice called.

Ben was the speaker for the post. Splendiferous news it was. The following persons to report to Phil's room the next day for collection of postcards from the POW camps and Red Cross (overseas). The cheers and olés could be heard from all sections of camp as the news was delivered. Even the unlucky ones joined in the hurrahs. The crowd disintegrated into a shambles of hugging bodies. It was almost too heady to believe Mother and I were two of the favoured ones, and we clung together feeling quite foolish as the tears streamed down our faces, grinning like clowns. Ben was swung into the mob for his share of hugging and kissing, especially as both he and Ruth were also on the morning roll call in Phil's room.

Rick very wisely did not ask for 'hush'. With Janie holding on to his free arm, we quietened down, waiting for Rick's announcement. This was unbelievable. Allowances from our contacts in the POW camps would be forwarded to us monthly, the first payment to be made with the mail. Rick went on to explain that the POWs were to be paid in military yen, according to their rank, and further, according to the amount of work they did outside their camps. The implication of the last bit of the sentence dawned upon us. A case of 'you, you and you will volunteer for whatever . . .' But that was to come later. For the moment nothing could possibly dim the shining promise of the mail to come.

Our exuberant Ben had the final goodnight words: 'The party's over girls and boys – back to barracks'!

Still chattering we went back to our rooms to digest the wonderful news of the day.

It was going to be a very long and sleepless night full of recapturing happy memories that had no time to collect dust. So many nights to be lovingly gloated over alone or among the special people who shared their dreams of happy times. The evening's excitement was becoming less noisy, everyone longing to share the good news and hear that other friends too had been lucky. Mother suggested that I slip over to

Suki's room. 'But please dear, don't be too late, in case the guards are on the prowl'!

Suki was leaning against the wall just round the corner of our corridor, talking quietly to Tony, her face aglow with happiness.

'Hi, join us for a draught of our favourite beverage and let's hear your news,' from Tony. We were tongue-tied for a moment, then, grabbing hands, did a jig. Tony looked at both of us, pointed to the teapot and mug on the sink, and with a nonchalant salute hurried out of sight. Then, taking advantage of Tony's hospitable teapot, Suki poured us half a mug of the good brew.

How we laughed at the bombardment of letters Jimmy must have rained on the Red Cross! Mother's letter, we hoped, would be from someone in the family. We had no idea where Father could possibly be after the fall of Singapore. Oh tomorrow, to-morrow, hurry, hurry, hurry. On my way back I reluctantly talked myself out of slipping down the slope to Joyce and Peg's pad. I tried to kid myself Mother would worry, but knew it was the terrifying prospect of being caught and dragged Up-The-Hill again.

Up at the crack of a welcome pale amber dawn to be ready for the distribution. Chores were being skimped through, swapping arranged to allow time to fit in the eager mail/allowance collectors to wait at the appointed places. Roll-call was boisterous and disorderly. Then the long-awaited worthwhile moment arrived. Phil came from the office, grinning and waving two handfuls of paper and went into his ground floor room, with the first group smartly on his heels.

To avoid further confusion it had been agreed at

167

the suggestion of the committee that the money-bit be sorted out that evening. The Japanese had consented to include a supply of extra fruit on the ration lorries, for sale at a minimum price. The monies would go to the hospital for much needed building up of the more serious cases. Thus Japanese generosity would not conflict with the black market!

The day galloped along in a scramble of meeting friends, exchanging news and somehow finding the mundane duties were automatically got through. Having collected our two cards, Mother and I sat together in a state of blissful euphoria. Mother's postcard was from the Colonel. Though it was a great kindness, we had hoped there would be news of Father. Nothing could spoil the answered prayer of those twenty five words from Himself, as Mother called my husband!

The morning meal slurped down, Suki, clutching 'my Jimmy', and I went racing off to the library, where Joyce and most of the gang would be visiting during opening hours. 'Just like old home week,' Peg quipped, 'gaggles of girls huddled over each other's bounty.' Most of the book borrowers slunk away after a jaundiced look at the state of the bar!

We did a roaring trade in gossip, but not much in the business of lending books. Joyce had a loving letter from her William, Peg from a dashing army boyfriend. The traffic was non-stop, and most of us met the friends we most wanted to see and hear their news. Thankfully the messages were comforting. Those who could read between the lines and detect a sadness thoughtfully hid their fears. There would be time enough to unburden the unhappiness.

It was going to take several days to sort out our pieces of news, to glean possible oblique references on the state of health and morale of the men. However it was more than likely they would strictly adhere to rules demanded for communication. No one could be as stupid as I was, even unwittingly risking a going over, which in their case would be by the dreaded Gendarmerie.

As most of the day had been taken up with the collection of postcards the line-up for our pay packets was postponed until the following day. The worried souls without news were terribly disappointed. The sender of the 'allowance' might be able to give a clue as to why no postcard. However, it was unlikely as all mail was strictly censored.

Pam, who was billeted up at St Stephen's, had searched me out in the library to show me her postcard. She was engaged to a captain, the same rank as David, also a close friend. Reggie had sent the interesting information on his card that '. . . receive very generous allowance sixty two yen . . .'

This meant that in my postcard which included, '. . . fifty yen follows . . .' all David had left was twelve yen. What on earth would that buy him, a toothpick for the non-existent meat rations?

My buoyancy rapidly deflated at the realisation of how little would be left from his 'generous' allowance. I joined the rest of the bodies waiting at Phil's door. The morning news was that the strongly doubted item of the extra fruit supplies for sale turned out to be true! Again, rosters had to be planned for the order in which purchases were to be made.

Supplies distributed to camp kitchens solved most of the problem. The colourful rows of bananas and oranges with a heap of local greens, not to be despised, made a mouth-watering selection. More so, as promises had been given that stocks would follow during the next few days, ensuring that most of us would have a chance to get our share. If not, being blessed with riches, there was always the black market!

I counted out the extraordinary looking paper money Phil handed me, baffled by arithmetic. There was one hundred yen. The solution, of course, had to be that the other officers in the regiment had made up David's pay to 100 yen. Here at least was a message that the other chaps were safe, as surely there would have been a deduction from the extra fifty yen, by numbers if any were missing by escape or, much more heart-breaking, death. Fervently hopes rose. Mother with her perpetual silver lining agreed. It was strange to be handling money – pretty ropey-looking but nevertheless, money! Just imagine the joy of knowing that all the boys were still together. What another great day.

Baldy-Balls-Up was positioned at one of the stalls of delicious wares, calling us to 'step up for three shies a yen'. His suntanned face was alive with fun as he carefully selected the items, according to the amount one was permitted to buy for each family! He kept us moving with his 'Hurry along there, ducks,' the already good-humoured crowd quipping back, 'Go on, you old horse-thief, hands off the goods'! As I reached Balls-Up he was juggling expertly with three oranges, which he returned to the row, and scooping me up in his gigantic right arm, he balanced me on his hip, giving his barker's call: 'For unlucky for some 'ere I 'ave the BOOBY prize!'

More snorts of derisive laughter, as I was gently lowered to select for my list of three persons. The choice was not difficult as stocks were already badly depleted! At that moment Billy came belting up to our market breathlessly yelling, 'Demolition squad coming!'

The sudden silence was as stunning as a physical blow. Billy, with a fiendish grin, clutched my waistband, hissing, 'It's the Formosans!'

These recently imported security agents were nasty provocative brutes. Like all converts, they wished to prove their allegiance to HIM Emperor, modelling themselves on the brutal behaviour of the Gendarmerie if given the slightest chance to take offence. Unlike old Humpty Dumpty or even Pisspot, they moved in pairs, and delighted in conjuring up an ugly situation. To all internees, the general order was to 'avoid and retreat' as hastily as possible.

The market continued, subdued, no banter just a quick buy and slope off. To everyone's amazement, on reaching our stall, these two mighty warriors took a quick look at proceedings, snatched a banana, tossed it at Billy and quick marched from whence they came. It was very much later that the reason for the Formosans' disinterest became clear. They had already had their bit of fun up at one of the bungalows, where they had booted over a carton of fruit. Inexcusably from Frank's point of view, they understood the universal four-letter word he spat at them. Having backed Frank against the bungalow's wall he was badly beaten up for the insult. Two of the women were singled out and forced to crawl round the premises retrieving the bruised fruit, to which the enemy helped themselves before marching off on route for further plunder.

Frank was a bloodied mess, attended to as well as the women could before alerting the hospital that he was being brought in. A very strong protest was made to Tanaka. To temper the undercurrent of rebellion,

171

the committee were told that the guards had been heavily disciplined and replaced. It was a victory for the weak side if little help to Frank, who had a fractured jaw to suffer along with the cuts and bruises.

Billy, the bloodthirsty little tyke, went to visit Frank. 'I want to give him my orange.' What the young chap wanted was first-hand information to boast of to the 'small fry'!

The year 1943 was opting out. Although the theatres of war news was excitingly encouraging through genuine reports from a new crop of radios, and the welcome sounds of air traffic more frequent, we had finally come to terms with the fact that there was to be no imminent release.

Despite the warning of no increase in rations, new crops of babies kept the maternity ward busy and families, friends and neighbours showed lively interest in the newcomers. It was a great event to attend a christening to which the guests and godparents managed somehow to present a gift. Our little coven, as Joyce had labelled us, had been encouraging a romance between Josie, one of our favourite hospital volunteers and Derek, an extremely shy young man who had only been in the colony about eight months before the European, then our, war had interrupted his apprenticeship with one of the banks.

In the very early days Derek had been attacked by the old dysentery bug. He had been really very ill indeed, and was in the hospital for quite a few weeks. On my night duty stints, after I had learned the lesson of the bottle, I had spent many a late night when Derek had been unable to sleep, chatting with him. There was a girl at home he loved desperately, but felt that during his long absence she was bound

172

to meet other young men, and in the circumstances war inevitably produced, couldn't help feeling she would not be waiting for him. Poor lad, he had come into camp strong, full of hope that the duration of the war would be short. Then he began to give way to despair, especially when his long bout of illness had sapped his strength, leaving him gaunt and dull-eyed, losing the will to live.

Josie was on the morning shift as I came off duty. We used to have a brief conference about the mental state of some of the patients. She felt strongly our role as amateurs was to boost the morale of the sick, the professionals being competent to look after their physical needs. Josie was certainly the right soul in that department. Gay, full of fun and quite lovely to look at. In fact I suspected she strongly resembled the girl Derek had left behind. So one morning, after Derek had had a particularly depressing night, I suggested that she concentrate on shaking him out of his gloom. Very gently the romance blossomed, and we all connived to keep the pot boiling.

When Derek left hospital after his second wretched attack we lured him into our circle, which included Josie. She had mothered him like a new born baby whilst he was bedridden, but became infuriatingly shy and elusive once he was back to quarters. After far too long a time Derek and Josie began to go off and do things together, not needing our crutches anymore. We thankfully awaited their betrothal. Incurably romantic, Suki kept bemoaning the lack of news.

'When will they tell us? We must have lots of time to save up for the wedding and the party after.'

Peg, always the practical one, retorted when she had got thoroughly sick of Suki's litany, 'Belt up, Suki, you're going to scare them apart with your match-making!'

Josie finally confided in Joyce, our senior member, that both she and Derek felt camp was not the place to make a momentous decision about the rest of their lives. They had decided to wait until they were free.

Sensible perhaps, but received with grave disapproval! Suki shed a few tears before devoting her energies to the event of the next arrival in the maternity ward.

With Christmas approaching again to plague so many with painful memories, Carol and our dauntless directors/producers felt they could tackle a pantomime. *Peter Pan* or *Cinderella*? Canvassing opinion, *Cinderella* won. The auditions began, and the camp was combed for available props. Stage hands were recruited. Artists produced sketches for costumes and scenery. It was an awesome challenge. Rehearsals had to be fitted in, the hall and club bespoken for practising the musical scores, prompters co-opted to 'hear' the principal's lines, the tailors hounded for suitable garments!

There was no shortage of talent or takers for the leading parts or chorus. Rick and Arthur, who had made a hilarious comic team in an earlier sketch, were cast as the Ugly Sisters. Suggestions were sketched for their make-up. In the end Rick, the taller of the two by far, was to wear a blond wig of shoulder length ringlets, cleverly fashioned from a skein of yellow wool. He was to play the simpering, easily affronted female. Poor Arthur, short and weedy, was to be bewigged in a black Dutch bob as the aggressive bossy sister. At most of the rehearsals, which had to be played in groups, there would be an enthusiastic following. The Ugly Sisters were so hysterically funny that they even collapsed themselves, incurring the producer's displeasure, when he could draw breath to call them to order!

A children's chorus too had been included in the show. Billy even condescended to do a few high kicks. They were a panic to watch, weaving in and out of time and tune, going the wrong way, or bumping into each other and rolling helplessly about with either shrieks of laughter or howls of temper at their clumsy sidekick. One had to be very circumspect not to double over with pain at a highly amusing, but mistaken antic. Carol let it be known that she would prefer that no 'unauthorised' persons gatecrash the children's time! A pity but one could appreciate her thinking. It was murder enough to cope with anxious parents, and willing but unruly performers!

The grand finale was to have a large Christmas tree in the middle of the proscenium with decorations, these to be made by volunteers. At the foot of the tree was a wrapped gift for each of the children, wrapping and gifts to be provided by donations. The children's chorus divided on either side of the tree, the rest of the cast making up the backdrop, Cinderella in her pumpkin carried on by the two Ugly Sisters – pretentious but possible.

It seemed that every last soul in camp was working feverishly on some project for the success of the pantomime. Even the King Pin had his flock of salesmen contribute enough amounts of wong tong bars, packets of peanuts and some Chinese sweet-meats for the children's parcels. Baldy-Balls-Up had a field day spreading propaganda that the con-science-offerings contained tummy-ache pills, thus forcing the parents to patronise their nearest com-prador for a pricey cure-all!

Permission was granted for a four-night stand – no

script censoring required. If our own producers had not censored the script, the ad-libbing would have required the show to be extended far into the night. The committee did their best to pin down the night when the illustrious Japanese would be in the front row. They were thwarted as the front two rows were reserved for each night. Much of the smut directed against the East Asia Co-Prosperity angle had to be deleted for safety's sake. Nevertheless some extremely satirical snide remarks were tossed in for camp audience appreciation. These created such bedlam that the performers either had to mime the action following, or wait for 'hush'!

Carol asked the committee to apply for one matinee for children only. The request was granted. There were two dress rehearsals sneaked in, which were fully attended. The matinee also a full house. One night's break. Then the four big nights, the last with the grand finale!

All seven performances were quite magnificent, outstandingly professional, and side-splittingly funny, was the consensus of opinion. The make-up artists, costumiers, scene and prop builders had all done a really wonderful job. Needless to say the Ugly Sisters and the kids' chorus completely stole the show. The finale was a real tear-jerker as the Good Fairy handed the children their Christmas gifts. The younger ones proceeded to rip theirs apart on stage while Billy-Boy tried to round them up before the curtain landed on the excited exhausted and bewildered future star material!

Our hosts had attended the last two nights and were suitably impressed. With surprising magnanimity they agreed that the tree could remain on stage until after Christmas Day. Carol singing would be allowed in the hall for the three nights preceding December 25. This was quite a concession as it meant that it would not be necessary to do the rounds except for the hospital visit.

The pandemonium backstage, rounding up the easily removed props, also the players to be escorted to the various billets, was almost as funny as the actual pantomime. To anyone who did not belong to the community it would surely look like a horde of tipsy revellers staggering home after a thick night out! The small group who lived in the building promised to keep an eye on the tree decorations, whilst many helpers offered to renew the leafy garlands as they wilted. There must have been acres of cardboard used for the stars, crescent moons and fairies. Red and blue paint was donated by courtesy of our small colony of artists. The fairy atop the tree was in sparkling silver tinsel conjured up from someone's stock of memorabilia. As the late leavers hurried home through a snoopy chill wind, the soft strains of 'God Save The King' could be heard on the piano, which Sybil had played through the show.

Unfortunately, although our population was increasing, the cemetery too was becoming overcrowded. Illnesses, and operations which normally would have stood at almost one hundred per cent recovery, did not always respond to the overworked hospital staff and doctors, the causes being lack of nutrition, drugs, and in some cases the lack of will to try and make it.

Coupled with this was the grievous confirmation that seven of our prisoners had been executed by the end of October. Four had been given long sentences, one had died in jail. These details had apparently been smuggled out of the jail by a loyal Indian warder who was certainly jeopardising his life by collaborating with the camp.

The unexpected surprise was Christms postcards delivered to and from our camp and the camps across the harbour. Mother and I had put Suki on our payroll. The following allowance, happily still in the amount of one hundred yen, was again a wonderful message. The three of us squandered this generous dividend in the black market, to squirrel away for our big feast of the year! The dreamers predicted it would be the last in captivity; the practical sages kept their views to themselves. One of the most objectional females was by ill chance in our block. Large as she had once been, now the flesh pleated round her body. Gravelly-voiced, bushy-eyebrowed, and thoroughly offensive, she would spread gloom, doom and destruction for us all within the coming year. She had originally been up in St Stephen's quarters, but was so overbearing, greedy and prone to resort to fisticuffs if thwarted, that she had been re-billeted. When our blockheads had been told the bad news we had declared war. Ours was a companionable, well-assorted little world, not to be landed with this evil bitch. Our authority ruled that we must accept the ferocious creature, and after a conference within our private ghetto the decision resolved itself. She would be housed on one of the landings, preferably near the President's own quarters! It was an unpopular choice for the President, but one which he had to put up with!

The wording for my Christmas postcard became a nightmare. The girls were very unhelpful. Their provoking suggestions would have landed me first in line for the execution squad! Biting of nail and chewing of pencil stub again. I fidgeted over what to write until it was 'last minute' for handing in. Hopefully the two words, 'Loving Greetings' could not possibly exercise the censors. The platitude was rewarded, there was no summons Up-The-Hill!

# 10

Having got over that hurdle the third year started uneventfully. Not all of us had been able to buy duck eggs before our allowance began, and after a couple of years of what one might call a bland diet, we found them particularly strong and fishy tasting, not very appetising. But it was a tremendous relief to be able to buy the odd duck egg, or slab of wong tong when the money rolled in. Mother was not addicted to the duck egg diet, but knew that apart from extra padding in the chow bowl, there must be some nutrition in them.

Although the unloved lodger of the landing seemed to be docile enough, and our overall hostility not quite so obvious, we were still on guard against her reputation of stirring the pudding. She made herself scarce most days, revisiting her old haunts. Phil wisely said that he would prefer us not to include her in any of our duty rosters. Ulla was her given name, but she remained the Unloved One amongst ourselves. It was cruel and unfriendly. As she had to use our kitchen line-up, which was always the scene for badinage, most of the neighbours made the effort to include her in the local conversations. She never spoke, she made STATEMENTS. She was not interested in the block gossip, it was too PETTY. Any chat about a new baby ws brushed aside as DIS-GUSTIN'.

It was hardly surprising the first time a new young mother appeared to collect her morning meal, that the Unloved One's claws were out in our presence. Mary was a pretty little soul who had been terribly upset when she found out that she was pregnant. Her boyfriend Kevin had not been able to afford the asking price of a tin of bully beef or cigarettes for one or more condoms. They doubtless would not have worked anyway, having been stowed away for quite some time. After Mary had got over the initial shock and all her friends had rallied round with kindness her daughter arrived safely, and was proudly adopted by us all. Mary had not been in residence when the battle whether to have, or not to have, the new occupant of our well-dug-in community was raging. Mary had naturally been told of the situation but was in such a state of euphoria it just did not sink in. So with a heightened sense of unease faces turned to watch as Mary got behind the Unloved One in the chow line striking up an introduction. For several days Mary took up her place behind the dragon, and we more or less accepted the situation. Myra had been talking to Kevin and told a few of us that Mary thought the Unloved One was a 'dear' and as we all seemed to be persecuting her, was planning to ask this dragon to be a godmother to their daughter. Mother of God, don't let it happen. It did. With the foregone conclusion!

A couple of days later, again in the chow line, Mary shyly told the line that Ulla was going to be the babe's godmother. While surprised but pleased the prospective godmother made the STATEMENT that the child was to bear HER name! 'OH no Ulla,' said Mary in a firm voice, 'my name first, yours second.' Our rice dispenser, a tough sly-eyed fellow, yelled out, 'So the poor kid's stuck with MUT, she sure will take after her Mum.'

That was when the rot set in.

'You horrid beast,' Mary shouted back, as the Unloved One's face froze before, crumpling like a gigantic cream cracker, she sat down abruptly, expelling noisy gasping sobs. As the sensitive Suki went to try and help her struggle up, she was knocked sideways with such force, being huffed at between gasps to 'get away from me, you filthy Jap'.

Mary ran howling to her block, chased by a chum. Several of us rushed to collect Suki off the ground. Ben and two other lads heaved the Unloved One to her feet, hauling her off to her landing with jeers from the kitchen staff, adding that her LUNCHEON would await her collection from the kitchen after the rest of us had been served.

By the time several of the blockheads had arrived to investigate what all the commotion was about the chow line was back in business. Myra rescued Suki's rice and veg tins, sending a very shocked and shaky Suki up to Mother. Kevin, the baby's father, had been told of the fracas, and spluttering with fury headed for Mary's room while one of Mary's room-mates was given her rations. Heads were hanging out of windows, anxious to see what the skirmish was about. No doubt an embellished version would do the rounds tonight.

The various assortment of tins and dishes were finally filled, the empties cleared off back to the kitchens. Myra, Suki and I sat together in the corridor, shovelling down the now cold and soggy meal. The sequel of the christening, which took place without the Unloved One some weeks later, was a rather strained affair. Although there was no Ulla amongst the child's name the very cuddly little thing was forever known in our block circles as 'The Mut'.

Winter seemed to be colder than ever remembered. Perhaps the blood was thinning faster through lack of sufficient calories. When not actually moving about or doing a manual job, the first priority was to get a fug up. As most of the quarters were bursting at the seams this was not too difficult, but the community rooms used for school, lectures, play and poetry readings, were riddled with unsuspected openings through which icy draughts swirled around. The library was the cosiest place to be with the shelves to the side and behind, and the bar across the front. There were many offers to stand-in for either Joyce or myself. The library committee felt that it would not be a good idea to enrol novices, as it meant they would have to learn the art of being security officers as well! By this time both Joyce and myself had acquired an automatic alarm system with regard to books unreturned, and where to track them down.

Smokers found that owing to a very short supply, cigarette prices were spiralling. Wally, the spiv, a narrow-faced joker sporting a prominent Adam's apple, started experimenting. He claimed to have found a very smokeable substitute for tobacco which he would market to the addicts for a fraction of the black market! As a few of the really desperate and impecunious types had been puffing on dried over-brewed tea-leaves, they agreed to give Wally's mixture a go. This was where the library unwittingly entered the deal. A few well thumbed Bibles, prayer books and reference books were popular with the older folk, who handled them with reverence, returning them on the due date. Our first clue that these editions were suddenly becoming of interest to characters to whom one would expect a torrid novel or detective books to be preferable, was when Wally, followed by a lewd inmate from the woodcutters, signed in with ingratiating smiles, one for a Bible and the other for a prayer book!

'Well I have now seen everything. Hope you can read words over four letters,' Joyce said sarcastically.

'Tetchy, oh guardian of the treasures,' spat back the lewd one.

'Freeze it, Jake,' Wally cracked at his chum steering him out of the hall. A few of those awaiting their turn sniggered. Lou, one of our staunchest supporters, muttered casually to the pair of us, 'Watch it kids, I don't fancy their choice.'

We tucked the warning into the back of our minds. Joyce, with Lou's remark stored away, decided to have a little snooping done by Mei, to whom all manner of information was shuttled. A subtle hint dropped amongst the boys would be sure to bring results of any misuse of the books.

In the passing weeks, not too frequently, more of these books were loaned out to more unlikely readers. Still no word from Mei. True the books were all returned on time, and on cursory examination were in no worse condition. We began to look less suspiciously at the borrowers until one afternoon, as we left after shutting up, Lou joined us. He asked if he could have a brief word inside the hall. It was empty except for a class of four or five art students in the far corner.

'Want to see the rabbit in the hat,' he said, his eyes twinkling. It was not a question for, without even a nod from either of us, he opened one of his very large fists and, holding it out to Joyce, offered her a cigarette! Sure enough this handmade smoke was rolled in a section of a page from a Bible. This was only noticeable after Lou had insisted that we both examine it closely, unrolling the fag.

The puzzle of the latest Bible-thumpers was solved. The supreme, blatant cheek had us sizzling with righteous fury. Joyce was ready to do immediate and bloody battle, backed by an army of book lovers who would also be against such vandalism. Lou had a much more devious plan, promising to help us carry it through. He explained that Wally had indeed found a smokeable substitute for the world's greatest tobacco producers – *pine needles* dried, crushed, moistened with a solution of wong tong and water. The finest paper in which to roll this nauseous mash was rice paper. The nearest paper to this could only be found in Bibles and prayer books as well as certain reference books in the library. Lou's plan worked with cunning and speed. Joyce, with her connection in the camp office, got permission from the President, through Japanese headquarters, for the three of us to open the library after curfew to stack the coveted remainder of these extremely popular books into a drawer in the president's office. We checked that only two were outstanding at that point. Lou said with an exaggerated shudder that he was thankful he had neither of them! We went through the list of the recent devotees and Joyce scored them off with a thick red crayon.

There were very few closely guarded secrets, and when word flared like a bush fire in every corner of the camp, the two unreturned issues turned up most mysteriously, but not one red-lined name appeared for further reading matter! Mei came up with her story when she knew that everything had been sorted out. Her husband would not allow her to divulge the culprit or the reasons, as in the queer code of the Blacks that would be grassing on the amateur opposition, which was an unfair advantage as they could not survive for very long anyway.

The next day was particularly uneventful. During off duty periods small bands of us were collecting firewood for our private 'burners'. The ingenious workshop had made literally dozens of wood burning cooking pots, called 'chatti', on which we were able to heat water or warm up left-overs. It was forbidden to cut down any wood that could be used in the kitchens but there was still enough fuel on the hillsides for scrounging. We were not encouraged to use these in the rooms for obvious reasons, although this rule was too often broken. The rooms with balconies or verandahs were usually willing to let the odd friendly neighbour use a corner for a brew-up. The Indian quarters and bungalows had their own facilities which made life almost civilized.

Most of Tom's 'syndicate', the village-raiders, would willingly help our coven to set up a reasonable stock of fuel while we in turn brewed up for them. The arrival of a fourth Red Cross parcel had been its usual morale booster that week – we were getting to know more or less the contents – always so welcome with the added excitement of sorting out what could be swapped with whom! Much in demand were the tins of bully beef, sardines, chocolate bars, condensed milk, never any more cigarettes. All the parcels had been 'censored' and of course the cigarettes were always missing. The Blacks were doing a roaring trade with them, also the odd parcel was minus one chocolate bar – somehow they did not appear with the Blacks' groceries. The faithful old 'cream of rice' was always there and becoming quite a favourite! So it was that Joyce voted that we have a mock curry muck-up on the following Sunday, only two days away. We would pool our rations, each provide a slice from a Red Cross tin of bully beef, perhaps some tinned fruit for sweet. Jan had the remains of a tin of curry powder he had got from one of his Chinese friends who managed to bring him a few small luxuries now and then. The rest of the boys donated a duck egg each. We girls made a pudding of rice flour, with a trickle of condensed milk, and a few slices of the tinned fruit. Between us we sorted out nuts, some prunes and dried coconut that had been saved up. As our Ben would say, 'Bob's Charlie's Aunt'! This cook-up would be held in the Indian quarters where it could be heated by sharing both Joyce and Peg's cooking areas. The planning took most of the evening; the anticipation ran a close second to the Sunday feast.

Just before going back to our blocks in time for curfew we heard excited voices coming down the path, talking about the bulletin board. The snippets of information were not loud enough to be clear, so Suki and I made a beeline to see for ourselves what it was all about. The notice post was surrounded by a crowd of people straining to read the message. As far as we could make out it was to do wth internees who held safety deposit boxes in the local banks. As neither Suki nor I were interested we left the mob to go and gather our contributions ready for the Sunday party.

Mother agreed that the Sunday party was a splendid idea, but said that she would prefer to eat quietly in the room. So it was arranged that I would

187

bring her share up, when it was ready. I knew it was an effort for her to go any distance as her legs were giving her a lot of trouble. The only cure was to rest them.

When the bridge players, and the bull session had got under way, I went to find Rick who was sure to be able to explain the latest message on the bulletin board. Rick and Phil, a member of the committee, were discussing the offer which had been made by Tokunaga, the Supreme Commander of all POWs and internees. In effect the message was that all internees who so wished, could give their safety deposit box number to headquarters, when the contents of same would be delivered to them in the camp!

'Sheer bloody fantasy,' was Rick's assessment.

'What possible reason could they have for such action?' queried Phil.

The pros and cons were bandied about, questions and answers of the probable result mulled over. As it was obvious the Japanese could rifle these boxes if they had not already done so any time they felt so inclined, most of the men were highly suspicious. Rick advised non-cooperation, adding that it was the individual's final decision.

Speculation as to the outcome of giving the number required was anybody's guess. Most of the guesses were extremely facetious, but gave an added spice to the characters concerned. Poor Rick was trapped for a simple deduction of this latest sophistry of Japanese thinking. He could only reply that he was as much in the dark as we all were.

The deadline for the list of numbers with names was the following Monday. This being, as always, Friday the people involved had time to talk it over and make their decision. All over the camp similar huddles of the lucky number owners were trying to gauge the reasoning behind the 'offer'. The majority agreed to take a chance, as what did they have to lose?

Sunday arrived for our lunch preparations in rose-coloured glasses! Finishing the morning chores we hurried down to Joyce and Peg, to leave our share of the banquet from our larders before collecting the morning rations. Mei was hovering around as I left the block, and pressing a tin under an arm, asked me to give it to Joyce with her love! Mei had heard the news of our Celebration Sunday, to which she generously added a batch of biscuits she had made especially for the occasion. On top of the biscuits was a short note asking Joyce's forgiveness for holding out on her over the book scandal! We all knew this was only an excuse for her wishing our enjoyment of the 'picnic' as she called it.

Lunch was a gourmet's delight! There was plenty to talk about with the final biscuit. Friday night's notice was still the focal point; as none of us had any part of the receiving end we let our imaginations go wild!

Tom came up with the Oscar! In his opinion the Blacks were going broke. In this way, all legitimate booty, tons of lovely gold bars and jewellery would be turned over to their rightful owners, which in turn would be flogged on the black market, for one hundredth of its worth, to shore up old stock, allowing the Blacks to replenish from the next batch of Red Cross parcels.

On Monday the list of names and numbers went Up-The-Hill. Now to wait for the purpose behind the offer. Everyone was baffled except Tom, who was sure he had the right and simple answer. 'The camp brains have so many devious theories, they can't think Oriental,' he grinned.

Several weeks followed, and the guessing game faded away with lack of further information. We were far more intrigued by the sudden batch of rumours about the victories in both the theatres of war. It really took so little to send our hopes soaring. 'Nineteen-forty-four, sigh no more,' was the latest theme song. The cautious Jeremiahs advising that there was still a hard slog ahead, failed to keep the wet blanket on us for long. The crowds at the community singing gatherings grew larger and more boisterous, despite frequent cuts in rations!

The notice so many had been holding their breath for, some with mixed feelings, arrived in bold black print, SAFETY DEPOSIT BOXES. The blockheads were given the names of persons to appear the next day after roll-call, at Tanaka's headquarters. Phil had only two names on his list. There were few wealthy tycoons in our little lot to boast about. Unsettling reports came from our Up-The-Hill watchers that evening. There had been noticeably more traffic on our main road during the day, which various people had commented on. Curious eyes kept a tally on whether the cars disappeared into the jail. This was the camp barometer, for should they so do, it meant terror for the hapless prisoners, infecting us all with dread. None of the traffic was reported as entering the jail, except the usual van with the change of guard or warders, plus the usual ration lorry. Nevertheless there was disquiet at Japanese headquarters. Tanaka was said to be in a filthy temper. Not a good omen for tomorrow's visit for the claimants of their 'box' possessions. Kate, one of our war widows who had sent in her name and number, admitted to Phil that in view of the mood in enemy territory, perhaps she could plead sick and forego the uncertain pleasure of collecting the few valuables she had left. Phil and her friends pointed out that it was one helluva time to get cold feet, as whatever had arrived would only be released to her. Longing to make a quick visit to find out if Joyce had any notions about the extra traffic that day, I was told by Tony, who guessed my thoughts, not to be a bloody fool. It did not take too much bullying to stifle the idea with tempers uncertain at Japanese headquarters.

Latterly, during the very cold periods of our winter, the kitchen staff throughout the camp had managed to produce hot congee, a rice gruel for the older members in their districts. The younger members would take it in turns to collect the gruel for their particular area. So it happened that the morning of the 'box' collectors, a group of us were in line with our tins, awaiting this appetiser. Carrying four small portions back, I met Florrie setting up her tools for peanut grinding on the landing where the stone mortar and pestle were for the convenience of the rice flour or peanut butter merchants. Victor, her boyfriend, who lived in the Indian quarters, had nipped up after curfew with the bag of peanuts she was to grind and also the interesting news that the fracas Up-The-Hill was indeed true, inspired by the arrival of the 'boxes'. Unfortunately my chat with Florrie considerably cooled down the gruel. Mother decided she would have to re-heat hers when a chance came to get the *chatti* going. Poor Mother, as it turned out it was a lucky delay. Having got the *chatti* going, on stirring her breakfast cereal, she found some added protein which was the unwelcome body of a baby rat! Not a very auspicious start to the day.

As we watched, the queues formed waiting to be summoned to collect the contents of their boxes. The camp was agog, unable to concentrate on the opening chores of the day until we heard the details first hand.

Everything, it appeared, was going along quite smoothly. The individual identified the property, signed for it in the presence of Tanaka, Miyake and two uniformed strangers, one of whom, pock-marked and pot-bellied, showed his authority by snarling at an unhappy looking Miyake, who would translate the snarls into petty orders, such as 'Hurry,' 'Keep in line,' 'Don't talk.'

Most of the internees, on receipt of their goods, were despatched back to their camp areas. The last lot were from the original American quarters. Amongst them was Daddy Brady. He was the universal baby-sitter. As his hands were cruelly crippled with arthritis he was unable to do any manual work. In his early seventies, tall but stooped, with a gleaming set of dentures, his elected job was to oversee the creche. New babies, semi-new babies in home-made prams, the toddlers and four-to five-year olds whose mothers had camp details work on would park them with Daddy Brady. The kids loved him. He would tell them gruesome stories of hell and destruction, rock the whiners to sleep, separate warring thugs, share out bits of wong tong, biscuits, whatever he could produce from his larder of Red Cross parcels. They were all loved by him. Practically every day there was a scene when mums or guardians arrived to collect the brats!

The catastrophe struck as he ambled up to the desk where he had gone Up-The-Hill. He was astounded at a screeching tirade from Pock-Face which, being translated, was to the effect that he had wasted the time of HIM Officers, and insulted the Camp Commandant Colonel Tanaka, by making foolish claims for his 'box'.

Miyake was running out of breath translating the dishonourable adjectives describing Daddy Brady's contents. Four large albums were produced by a guard. They were dropped onto the floor in front of him and kicked open. Stamps.

'To what purpose did these bits of paper relate – ANSWER.'

'They are my savings for the future.' Daddy Brady was trembling.

'You have no future, but because of your senility and infirmity we shall not punish you physically, nor sentence you to jail. Step aside until I am ready to deal with you.'

Two guards hauled him off roughly to the back of the room whilst the rest of the claimants, by now cowed by this insane exhibition, gathered up their belongings. Instead of being dismissed they were told to remain to hear the penance this senile old fellow prisoner would have to make. Pock-Face handed a long scroll to Miyake, who in turn handed it to Tanaka, by this time his face a deep sepia. Daddy Brady was permitted to walk back to face Pock-Face and Tanaka. A guard either side of him, his pain-wracked eyes looked down at his tormentors. They all listened whilst the Colonel solemnly, slowly and with obvious relish read out the sentence. This was then translated by a sweating Miyake. One of the women started to sob, as Daddy Brady's arthritic hands covered his face with tears welling through the crippled fingers.

Enough, the baiting was over. The officers left abruptly. The remaining internees were ordered out by the No. 1 guard, leaving three others to escort Daddy Brady, carrying his precious cargo of albums, cradled in his arms, to the guard room where he was to complete his penance.

The barbaric sentence caused a near riot in the camp, though the president, with the help of Guy, tried to intervene. They were dismissed. There was to be no substitute sentence. The matter was closed, Colonel Tanaka had spoken.

Daddy Brady was to tear up each album page by page, the remains of which he personally was to feed into the well-fired rubbish dump behind the guard room.

Guy was allowed to bring poor devastated Daddy Brady back down the Hill. His room-mates thoughtfully left him alone. Kind Dr Stuart waited for him with a sedative. A sullen, dangerously near-rebellious crowd were told of the consequences should trouble erupt.

For two days Daddy Brady did not appear to baby sit. The kids catching the subdued feeling of fury running through the grown-ups, huddled together for those two mornings with an unenviable volunteer to watch over them.

When Daddy Brady surfaced he went back to his beloved kids. The kids leapt all over him like kittens – crawling onto his lap and almost throttling him with love. Some of the hurt went from his eyes, and he cheered up quite remarkably in view of the torment he must have gone through. All the mums got together and made him a good-sized cake with 'Welcome Back' across the top. He perked up and insisted on sharing it with his tribe at their chow time. Our mentor, Billy-Boy, was there to help distribute the tasty morsels! The heart-breaking sentence was never referred to again. Of necessity the volcanic rumblings in the camp subsided. However, frustration at our impotence burned throughout all the communities for a longer period than previously. The powers Up-The-Hill were very aware of their mishandling of the situation and they played down their presence in full battle-kit for a brief period.

# 11

The cold weather continued to be more tedious than we remembered. We spent the time in between endless boring work shifts trying to thaw out. Tempers were scratchy and arguments flared up over petty thoughtlessness. We were surrounded by colds, coughs and protesting joints. The lovely hot spells on the beach, the sultry summer nights were faraway dreams. The general wail of, 'Oh for the prickly heat' got the bitter response of, 'If we live that long!' But at least nature could be relied on to continue her seasons cycle.

Tom and his syndicate were in training for the coming months. Under-the-wire expeditions had become disappointing as far as producing the spoils. The murderous Gendarmerie were more alert. They had clearly been tipped off that forays were being made into the village from time to time. The disadvantage our boys suffered was that it was impossible to disguise themselves as the locals, who had played such a vital part in these raiding trips. The danger to the villagers was far greater than to a handful of internees. If they were suspected of any collaboration it meant their whole family, perhaps the whole village would suffer.

It was alarmingly obvious to the committee that

activities amongst the fisherfolk were slowing down. Although the rumours in the form of news of the outside world were much more encouraging, one could not help feeling that with the joys of summer on the way it could for the most part be wishful thinking – better to encourage the cheerful hopes.

Peg confided to me that Jan, our young Dutch friend, was recently very much in evidence during the syndicate's plotting periods as Tom jokingly referred to the 'men only' evenings. She was afraid that the informers would also notice this and suspect something diabolical was in the planning stage. Knowing Tom's cunning she tried to shrug off the little demon of fear. The whole sordid world we battled to survive in would pass with winter's cold clammy fingers prying out common sense.

Carol and her cohorts were busy planning an end of season *Panorama*. This was to be a medley of cabaret, short comic sketches, a brief mime of Queen Victoria's Jubilee ending up with Betty on the piano playing requests for us all to join in. Rehearsals were slow to start. It was difficult to drum up the usual enthusiasm. Carol and her gang tried hard to break through the apathy. When they had exhausted all patience they said they had decided to abandon the idea, we could get on with our miseries! That was the shot in the arm we needed. There was a burst of vigour and everyone taking part worked fiendishly to meet the proposed opening date.

The depressing atmosphere was banished. Fun and laughter were back with everyone eager to play a part in making the show a huge success.

There was to be a surprise item, the secret closely guarded with the entire cast's cooperation. Carol rehearsed the 'scene' as two separate entities so that the punch line would be dramatic!

The curtain rose on a chorus of six beautifully trained ballet dancers, the pick of Carol's two years' hard work. The music being Romeo and Juliet, the first few minutes were beautiful to watch. The audience were completely absorbed. As the chorus draped themselves gracefully round the stage, the two young lovers literally tripped towards each other from either side of the wings.

Baldy-Balls-Up was Juliette, the Dutch bob-wig, worn by the Ugly Sister in Cinderella, fluttering coyly. Bottom, under the blonde ringlets Romeo, leapt in ungainly strides towards his love, hitching at his Roman trousers which threatened to hit the deck! Then began their romantic dance of love, thanks to choreography by Carol.

This had to be the funniest act ever played anywhere! Even the graceful chorus were laughing helplessly as Baldy and Bottom pirouetted, and made loving overtures to each other. They too were panting with suppressed mirth. Bottom's trousers collapsed around his enormous bare feet, exposing a magnificent pair of silver lamé underpants, fashioned out of someone's long-treasured evening dress! Baldy lost his Dutch bob, snatched the blonde ringlets off Bottom's head, and hauling Bottom in a fireman's lift, tippy-toed through the swaying chorus. With a wave of a large hairy arm, they disappeared as the curtain came down with the band playing a discordant dirge!

It took a long time that night for the camp to settle down. We only had to conjure up the ballet to go into painful convulsions of laughter. The planned finale, with Betty at the piano, her requests lined up, had to be cancelled. No one had enough air left for singing, and anyhow the time limit for out-of-bounds was long since up.

Dr Stuart made a special request for the ballet scene to be staged at the hospital for staff and patients fit enough to stand a belly-laugh. It was quite an undertaking. Carol supervised the setting in the larger of the two top wards. Those patients able to sit up were arranged on the foot of the beds of convalescing chums. The women patients, also ambulatory, came to join in, and all the hospital staff were delighted to help in the arranging of the audience. It was a terrific success and Dr Stuart said it was the best medicine that had ever been prescribed!

His heady taste of stardom made Baldy quite insufferable for a short interval. Although he soon came down to earth without his greasepaint and supporting cast, he developed a tendency to hoist unsuspecting females in the chow line over his shoulder, and dump them at the end of the queue. This was rapidly discouraged! Bottom, being a seasoned 'actor' owing to his part in *A Midsummer Night's Dream,* nonchalantly disclaimed any kudos for the hilarious dance of love!

There was time now to prepare for that long-awaited summer and the rains. Pray no typhoon. The children had shot up alarmingly, keeping the tailors busy. Billy had forsaken his small fry, and teamed up with the bigger boys. He still found time to search me out to relate the school gossip and brag about his marks. But he was never too grand to go to the aid of a youngster being bullied. He had given up guard-baiting for the more serious sport of boxing. He planned to be the world champion when he was a man!

Things were becoming a little tight in the way of a

variety in the ration of vegetables. The camp garden could not supply the entire circuit with many of the luxuries they grew in the way of tomatoes or potatoes. However, there was a good supply of garlic to flavour the stews and keep the insides disinfected. Many of the garlic addicts exuded the odour from their skins, and it was not always pleasant to be in close contact with them! Another luxury that had entirely disappeared for the majority was toothpaste, but the wood ash was just as effective. Soap was virtually unobtainable, even from the Blacks, yet somehow, apart from the incorrigible dirty-dicks, we managed to keep the lice from an invasion. Camp beds had to be de-bedbugged, a distasteful job. So the advent of a long hot summer, with an ocean of sea water at our doorstep, was a welcome joy on the horizon. We had been warned that sharks had been sighted in our waters towards the end of the previous summer, so to be very much on the lookout during the swimming season. This was scoffed at by most of the pre-war bathers, as there had never before been any sign of these predatory creatures around the Island, nor in the waters of the mainland.

The summer was also the time when news from the fisherfolk was fairly regular. No junks were allowed within hailing distance of the camp. However, on dark moonless nights, should the chief deliverer of news from Wei Chow find it possible, a messenger would crab his way around the rocks to as near the beach as was safe, leaving the news at some pre-arranged site, where our collector would find it. It was an extremely dicey operation, but the Allies' successes gave an added spur to the danger. Naturally secrecy was essential and less than a handful of our intrepids kept it.

200

Local parcels were less frequent as Japanese fishing was being badly mauled, making it difficult to bring in supplies. A few faithfuls still seemed able to scrounge necessities for their particular friends in camp. No one in our block had ever been called to collect at the monthly hand-outs, so there was great excitement and curiosity when a rather morose gentleman from one of the rooms was told to appear at the gate one morning. He was only referred to as the Pasha by his room-mates. Around sixty odd, his once tubby frame was now covered in loose folds of shrinking flesh; he was hardly known to utter other than 'Pshaw'. The irony that he should receive a parcel was compounded by the fact that he had NEVER opened one of his Red Cross parcels. These were stored under his bed for the proverbial rainy day, jealously guarded. He only left the room for the chow line or the call of nature. In the summer evenings he occasionally did a chukker round the block, but only when one of the other roomers would promise to watch his hoard!

So this local package, which was probably gathered through great hardship, would no doubt join the veteran Red Cross survival kits. By the time the Pasha had alerted his hoard-watcher, and hobbled down to the gate, the whole block was agog. A lookout was posted as near the main gate as was allowed for a non-receiver of a parcel to see if his gift was opened by the Gendarmerie. As he was a new boy, it was a certainty. The lookout might get a glimpse of the contents or even perhaps recognise the donor. A new piece of gossip to chew on.

Word finally arrived that the Pasha's parcel had been opened and minutely pawed over. It contained a bundle of noodles! The donor was a seedy-looking

201

elderly Chinese who looked as if he could do with a good meal of the noodles himself. It was reported later that the Pasha had actually curled a thin lip into the semblance of a smile as he added the re-wrapped parcel to his larder!

The poor old guy was in a constant state of panic that he might get ill enough to be carted into hospital, leaving his private store to be ransacked. His worst terror came true towards the beginning of summer when he actually forced himself to allow the bundle of noodles to be given to the hospital kitchen for his use only! Needless worry over his supplies plagued his nerves. On his return they were still under his bed untouched, with a chit attached which read, 'Perhaps three strands of noodles to each occupant of the room as custodian fee would be appropriate!' They knew of course that there were no noodles left.

The cloudless days of our freedom on the beach had finally dawned. Everyone livened up. The happy water-queues began the bucket line to the sea. The long-legged teenagers, the boisterous youngsters, and even the cuddly babies, carried by their mums for their first dip, were back to the carnival spirit. Less menacing, the guards showed a lack of discipline by helping to carry the smaller children down the steps. The youngsters who remembered the lovely pool from long ago begged to be able to use it. This was still taboo. Our little island looked invitingly green and tempting after the winter browns. At each beach session an internee was posted at either end of the cove to watch for the predatory shark. This summer no interest was shown by the garrison on the far point. Our faded bikinis over stick-insect bodies held no allure!

With the warmer evenings the walk via Siberia

became a series of sidewalk cafes. Friends from the bungalows and St Stephen's would join in a squat along the route with an after-supper snack to nibble, and news to be exchanged. Young lovers took to their favourite bush, and younger bands of searchers after 'pollination' makers disturbed many a romantic interlude! In spite of the repeated order forbidding newcomers, the roofs lured their quota when the brief twilight left darkness and anonymity to follow.

Peg's worries about Tom's syndicate and about Jan being included, grew increasingly strong. She tried not to discuss her fears with me, but needed to talk it out and perhaps convince herself that she was over reacting.

Jan spent much more of our alloted time at the beach than last summer. He was a very powerful swimmer, methodically exercising the length of the beach and back, more than once each day. He was also able to swim underwater for considerable periods. The children were all eager for lessons. With Jan appointed as instructor, his pupils quickly became able to keep themselves afloat and busy practising for the end of summer swimming galas, which the sports committee decided would be fun for the kids to look forward to.

Much to our dismay, the Gendarmerie, absent from the beach scene last year, had taken to planting themselves at the top of the steps. There a pair of them would stand watching our antics. This did not happen very often, but was disturbing, as normally the camp precincts were not their territory unless a grave offence had occurred. Peg became keenly aware that on their arrival, if Jan was in the sea, he would lope out lazily and park himself under the lee of the bank, out of sight of the steps. The squeals of the young begging for more instructions were ignored, until someone might casually mention that the Gendarmerie jerks had left. Peg asked me to confirm this should I be on the beach at a time when they appeared, and Jan was in the water. She wanted to be sure that she was not letting her imagination delude her. Peg was right. The only time I witnessed the Gendarmerie appear whilst Jan and I were chatting, at about knee-deep for me, a non-swimmer, he turned abruptly and picked his way up the sand to his pitch below the bank.

Short of teasing an explanation out of Jan as to a possible connection between the arrival of the Gendarmerie and Jan's retreat, we would never know the answer. Peg tried to draw Tom out talking about Jan, and his prowess in the sea. Tom just grunted, changing the subject.

Peg had a thorough knowledge of first aid, and kept a kit in her room to treat minor cuts and abrasions. When Tom and his boys were doing their sporadic flits under the wire to forage from the nearby villagers, this kit had come in handy on more than one nightly return. Since the raids had been abandoned, Peg's main medical treatment was for the kids, or the odd minor accident to a woodcutter, or kitchen staff.

The first aid kit was now becoming very low, as were all medicines in the camp. The doctors were particularly worried since the smugglers had been stopped. Even the Blacks were having difficulties getting supplies of vital drugs. There would have to be an appeal launched Up-The-Hill for their co-operation. Our President was approached but was unwilling to tackle the Commandant until he had ascertained the climate of the Great Man.

As the summer nights steamed peacefully by, Peg's fears calmed, and the talk reverted to the mundane day's activities, the latest rumour, and the ever present question, 'When would we be free?' It was encouraging to hear the heavy drone of aircraft passing over, out of range. of any anti-aircraft, even more frequently. The tempers of our captors were uncertain. Everyone was constantly reminded not to give them any provocation for reprisals.

An ugly scene was building up in camp. Those in high places felt we needed a change in our own hierarchy. They felt the present stand was not positive enough. The word went round that we should have a ballot. There were a couple of popular and willing candidates, but the very definite majority favoured Guy – he was so evidently the natural choice. We were all canvassed by our blockheads. Guy was very willing to be our candidate if voted for by a majority, and our President in command agreed. Everyone agreed that it was time for a change at the top, and so the camp committee was asked to convene a meeting. Days went by, and most of the conversation was about our forthcoming election. Alas, there then appeared on our bulletin board the following notice:

'All internees voting against our President will be noted for the record to be handed over to the British Government after the cessation of the present situation as TRAITORS!'

You can imagine our stunned reaction. Guy at once announced that he withdrew his nomination, as did the other two.

Strangely, there was no reaction whatsoever from our hosts. The notice was taken down after it had been digested – and apart from a few hotheads rustling up trouble, which fortunately was silenced with great haste, that was the end of our non-election. Mysterious, but no explanations given and none asked for.

# 12

The Chinese, great lovers of intrigue and past masters at deception, continued to plan ways of getting news from the outside into the camp, Tom's syndicate being one of the sources receiving messages with the blessing of the President. This was never acknowledged. As the greater part of the population were principally concerned with their own survival, very infrequent curiosity was shown as to where or how the pieces of news were passed through the camp. Much of it was dismissed as rumour. The authentic messages were naturally not relayed for safety's sake, so that many of the garbled stories of the beating the Japanese were taking were ignored.

About two hours before dawn began the awesome fateful day of that summer. Peg was awakened by Tom who whispered for her to gather her first aid kit, her darkest pair of slacks and a head covering and meet him on her back stoop. She knew that something disastrous, the something that she had subconsciously feared, had finally happened. She also knew that Tom would never endanger her unless it was a matter of life or death. He quietly explained in the darkness that they must get to his room. The safest way would be to dodge round the back of the blocks, which left the comparatively short distance of an open area in front of the club to slip across. The next hazard was to cover the line behind his block, to his room at the end, on the ground floor.

Peg had no time to be frightened, her thinking process was numbed. They made the journey in a matter of minutes, the ground being all too familiar. Peg was instinctively aware that the lights of the fishing junks and sampans in the bay were out, and the nightly barking of the fleet's guard dogs intermittent.

One of Tom's room-mates was fixing a blanket over the open frontage. One other figure was sitting propped against a wall. A very faint torch was switched onto the figure. It was Jan, glistening wet with dark pink water trickling down his left shoulder to merge with another darker pink flood at his forearm. Peg began to work on the ghastly wounds. Tom had produced some strong rice wine to clean the arm and what clothing there was in the room, to use as bandages. She gave Tom two aspirins to crumble into water and get Jan to drink. When she had done the best she could with her small supply of cotton wool, and now empty tin of sulphur powder, the torch was turned off. The other two members of the syndicate came quietly in, telling Tom that the hole in the sand under the wire had been filled in. They had, they hoped, successfully covered with sand the blood stains leading from the beach. As Peg asked about the cause of the accident, the Indian quarters slept on, the bay was silent, and dawn was showing her welcome to the coming day.

The story was told in quick concise syllables. A signal from the fleet master's junk, earlier in the evening, meant that he had news of momentous value. Jan was to swim out to the junk, assisted through the smaller vessels by one of the junior crew. Jan would be given this vital information, as it was too important to try and hide in message form near the beach.

The bay was gradually full of the anchored fleet, the cooking pots making the evening meal. The children were swimming around the boats, some going ashore to help peg out the fishing nets for drying, and the cacophony of the nightly chorus of yapping dogs starting up.

Tom and Jan had smeared themselves with black boot polish, reserves from the disastrous canteen, and the mission was launched as soon as it was dark enough. There was still enough chatter and movement in the bay to mask the launching of Jan off the far side where the water was deepest. The underwater swim to reach the first few anchored sampans, where his pilot was waiting, presented no difficulty. Then amidst the confusion of the night's comings and goings, Jan safely made starboard, facing away from the village. His pilot shouldered him up to the deck and he threw his left arm over the side for leverage when the unexpected happened too quickly to avoid. The guard dog, smelling a stranger, too excited to heed his master, snapped his rope and lunged at Jan's shoulder, then at his arm, before being torn off by the rest of the junk people. The only possible solution was to get Jan back ashore, to the safety of his mates, before he lost too much blood. The master whispered the message. A sampan was brought quietly alongside. Jan was lowered lengthwise in the bows and the agonising voyage back was skilfully completed. Tom was by now lying in wait amongst the rocks, knowing that things had gone terribly wrong.

Sid, one of the syndicate who was on alert, watched

with horror as Jan was off-loaded into the water as near as possible to the shore. Sid joined Tom to help bring the obviously injured man back to the room. This manoeuvre was a long slow process, with several stops to allow Jan to rest awhile. The bay suddenly grew very noisy, with laughter and shouting and barking of dogs. Tom and Sid realised this had been engineered as a diversion, and taking full advantage, at last got Jan and themselves through the sand hole under the wire into the room.

Only after waiting an hour to listen for any suspicious movements from the Japanese, did the bay quieten down for the night.

The enormity of the misfortune and the possible repercussions filled them with despair. Tom assumed full responsibility and worked out a plan. The moment the early morning crews began moving off to their alloted duties, Peg was to slip back to her room. Sid was to contact Dutch quarters, letting their blockhead know that Jan had missed the curfew so stayed the night in their room. Tom would go directly to the President's office to report the night's events. It was essential that Jan be taken to hospital. The greatest fear, of course, was that the dog might have contracted rabies.

A council of war was called by the President. The camp medicos were hastily sent for. The doctors were appalled, announcing that there was no anti-rabies vaccine in the hospital. The patient would have a maximum of forty-eight hours before needing the vaccine should the dog be rabid.

The first priority was to ensure that the Fleet Master remained in the bay, keeping a twenty-four-hour watch on the dog for any signs of the symptoms of this ghastly killer disease. The scheme had to be put into effect immediately.

Knowing the fear the Japanese had of any infectious epidemic, the doctors decided that they must send word to Tanaka that it was vital one of them be allowed to speak to Tanaka privately. Guy would accompany the doctor who would appeal for quantities of cholera vaccine, and other drugs of which the hospital was desperately short, or completely lacking. Should Tanaka agree to a doctor himself going to the Government Hospital, where many of the loyal staff were still employed, the doctor was reasonably certain he could obtain the anti-rabies serum without raising any suspicion. If not, the only alternative was to offer the King Pin a guarantee covering whatever amount he specified, to handle the entire operation. There was no alternative solution. King Pin's secrecy would have to be chanced. Speed was the primary factor.

Guy went off with the urgent message. In the meantime some way must be found to keep the fleet in port. Tom suggested that one of the police, some of whom spoke the fisherfolk's dialect, be appointed to talk to the Fleet Master, preferably in the camp's office, of the seriousness of a cholera epidemic, and that his fleet must not put to sea until it was absolutely certain that the case in camp had been isolated, and no infection spread. At least two days of close observation would be necessary. The village mayor, too, would be asked to report any sudden sickness to the Japanese medical authorities.

What a complicated web there was to weave! The bamboo wireless was already beginning to hum. One of the doctors hurried down to the hospital to alert the two senior nurses for the clearance of one of the small store rooms to receive a seriously ill patient. Jan had been answered for at the fortunately now not

211

very strict roll-call!

Miyake arrived to tell the President he was wanted in Tanaka's office. One of the Japanese doctors from the garrison had also been sent for. Guy had pleaded Dr Stuart's case firmly and eloquently. The decision was made by the Japanese doctor. He would go with Dr Stuart, with whom he had held meetings on the hygiene and several minor epidemics in the camp. A list of the badly depleted store of drugs was made, signed by Tanaka and the Japanese doctor who would inspect the supply to be issued to Dr Stuart. Miyake and Guy would also be in the drug raiding party. The car which would take them to the main Government Hospital, would be followed by a second car with two armed guards. The first hurdle was over.

Permission was finally granted for the patient suspected of having the symptoms of cholera, to be moved immediately into isolation in the hospital. No guard escort would be needed. The President then suggested the warning to both village and fishing fleet. By now Tanaka was thoroughly scared. He agreed that both the village mayor, and Fleet Master be called to the camp office, not headquarters, and the matter explained. An officer of the Gendarmerie was to be present. Hurdle number two.

As the cars sped down the road, watched by puzzled groups of internees, Tom, who was waiting for the return of the President and Tanaka's decision, saw King Pin in the car following, sandwiched between two guards.

If the charade of a possible cholera epidemic was to be kept up, a mighty amount of the vaccine would have to be collected – at any rate to cover Jan's block. At the end of the forty eight hours, if the all clear for rabies was given – God Bless Us. Then the medicos would have to find an answer for the 'severely' sick patient. That hurdle would be very happily crossed – the main object was to keep the camp entirely ignorant of the whole nightmare. Rumours, of course, were already spreading like the proverbial wildfire – but it was encouraged to counter any talk of epidemics as Japanese propaganda to cover any good news coming into camp regarding the triumphs of the Allies.

An order went to all blockheads to make sure everyone carried on as usual. An announcement would be made, should it be felt necessary, that evening. The camp was bristling with curiosity and rumour, plus a certain amount of real fear.

The interview with the two Chinese from the village was to be reported to Tanaka. Tom was chosen by the President to tell them of the circumstances. The President had faith in Tom being able to get the message over to the Fleet Master. It was a grave responsibility. An officer and NCO from the Gendarmerie duly arrived with the two impassive Chinese gentlemen. Tom made his speech stressing the 'no panic' factor. They were both assured that Japanese medical authorities would make the vaccine available to their people. There were no questions asked, but Tom felt a rush of relief and gratitude as the Fleet Master said, 'I understand.' Hurdle number three provisionally cleared.

Now came the agonising wait for the return of the medical team. Tom was trying to figure out where the King Pin came into the picture. Was it coincidence that he was also bound out of camp, or had he heard some whisper and was plotting some diabolical scheme. However, as it was commonly known that he made trips into town, Tom shelved the nagging

213

thoughts.

Jan had been quietly taken into the hospital, swathed in a blanket. Peg collapsed with exhaustion, falling into a deep sleep. The office settled down to the daily routine with the NCO stationed on guard at the door of the suspected 'cholera' patient.

To Tom the catastrophic events of the night before were not yet over, although with a great deal of optimism they were perhaps in hand. For the first time in many years, he prayed to the Virgin of Mercy to succour the camp and our loyal Chinese compatriots.

Late that afternoon the two cars returned, driving Up-The-Hill. Once again our President was sent for. Tom waited near the office, drained of emotion. After a short while a solemn group came down the steps. Dr Stuart, grey with fatigue and carrying a fairly large carton, made his way to the hospital, accompanied by the Japanese doctor. There was no way of guessing whether the mission had been successful. Tom watched the two doctors arrive at the hospital entrance. Dr Stuart saluted the Japanese doctor who returned the salute, turned sharply on his heel and made his way back Up-The-Hill.

As invariably happened, a crisis was sensed throughout the camp. The mood was subdued, but speculation rife. Tom was so intent on watching the arrival of the first car, that he failed to notice whether the King Pin was in the second car with the guards. The President spoke a few words to the effect that he would call Tom later, as he passed into the office.

The evening struggled on painfully. Sid managed to make Tom eat part of his day's ration. Just before curfew the blockheads told their charges that there was a suspected case of cholera in the hospital, but

214

sufficient vaccine had been brought in for inoculations. To Tom, the two words 'Sufficient Vaccine' comprised the message he had prayed so ardently for. He must reassure Peg and the boys before he took to his cot for a less troubled sleep. Tomorrow and the day after the signal from the Fleet Master would come. Should it be the danger signal, then another crisis would have to be faced, as to how to get to the Fleet Master, his family and crew who must also be given the serum. That hurdle, the steepest one left, he would think about tomorrow.

Dr Stuart's report on their visit to the hospital was in great detail. Before leaving camp, Dr Namura telephoned the doctor in charge of the Government Hospital warning of their arrival briefly stating the purpose of the exercise. Both Namura and Guy chatted amicably during the drive. Dr Stuart was too preoccupied to be interested in the well-known landmarks. He was excited at the thought of seeing Miss Chiu, the Chinese matron for whom he had the greatest respect. He wondered how many of the old gang would still be there. Memories came flooding back of the early days before the war, when he was still working in the hospital, before he had been interned. His main thought was whether it would be possible to achieve his object.

Coming down the last stretch of road he saw the tall impressive building where he had spent so many useful years. The driveway and grounds were the same with grassy lawns and slopes banked by colourful flowering shrubs. All still in perfect condition. At the main entrance the senior staff stood trim and starched. The matron, Miss Chui, Rosie to the doctors, looked her bright-eyed self, less plump, cheeks less pink, but her wide happy smile as he

215

stepped out of the car was worth all the difficulties to come.

Introductions were made. On entering matron's office Dr Namura was shown the schedule that had been drawn up for the visitors to take place when their business had been completed. Tea was brought by an orderly, and Dr Namura explained to Dr Ennosuke, the doctor in charge at the hospital, that Dr Stuart had a list of drugs and instruments badly needed in the camp, which he had official permission to take back with him. These items would be checked by Dr Ennosuke and his full cooperation would be appreciated. There was much bowing and sucking of teeth. Matron had arranged for her Head Sister to show Dr Namura and Guy around the wards whilst Miyake would go with herself and the two doctors to collect the listed items.

Dr Stuart was not surprised at the methodical way the vast store rooms were still arranged. Rosie was ever a stickler for orderliness. The list and amounts required were noted slowly and carefully by Dr Ennosuke. His eyebrows, a pencil line on his smooth, young-looking face, were frequently raised as he went down the list. Miyake explaining to Dr Stuart that several amounts would have to be trimmed. Rosie was efficiently lining up the drugs, vitamins and medicines as Dr Ennosuke called them out. He was obviously puzzled by the one item of anti-rabies vaccine, enough for several dosages over the required period. Dr Stuart was now to be put to the supreme test. Would the excuse for this item be accepted? Miyake, translating Ennosuke's words, asked Dr Stuart the reason for this unusual item. Dr Stuart suddenly felt a cold claw churning up his stomach. Looking firmly at Dr Ennosuke, he asked Miyake to

216

be good enough to explain to the good doctor that it was only included as a very unlikely reserve and precautionary measure. As Miyake knew, the Gendarmerie kept very fierce guard dogs, which they brought with them at times through the camp when visiting the jail. The children would sometimes crowd around the dogs, wanting to pet them. In the event one of the children got bitten, it would be prudent to have the vaccine on hand. The Gendarmerie headquarters were immediately outside the camp's main gate, and the village wonks could be seen sniffing around for scraps of food. They were the danger.

Miyake, looking startled at this turn in smooth sorting out of the supplies, delivered the translation earnestly to Ennosuke. Rosie, with a slight waver in her voice, asked how many children there were in camp, and generally tried to create a diversion. Dr Stuart laughed quite naturally, he hoped, and said there were too many, but without the supply of condoms it was difficult to keep the numbers down. Turning to Ennosuke he suggested jokingly that perhaps Dr Ennosuke would be kind enough to add that item to the list. Ennosuke joined in the jocular badinage, saying that he had four such young in his family, and it was indeed a full time job for his wife to keep track of them all at once! Rosie was to see if it was possible to include the items Dr Stuart had so boldly suggested. The checking off continued. Dr Stuart swore he could feel the touch of angel's wings across his face.

Ennosuke began asking the usual medical questions as to the care of patients, types of operations performed under difficult conditions, and ended up by saying that he would like to pay the camp hospital a visit. Dr Stuart said he would be delighted and

217

honoured. He was sure Dr Namura would be able to arrange this with their Commandant.

Rosie was busy filling the carton, and arranging with one of her sisters to collect dressings and disinfectant to be packed separately. They left the vast room, Rosie double-locking the door, and took the lift down to join the others in her office. Ennosuke was brimming with goodwill. He said he was sure that Dr Stuart would like to visit their only European patient at the moment, an Irish lady who had had a mastectomy, but first some tea to refresh themselves. He led them into his own office, sending for Namura and Guy to take tea with them. This was the very last thing Dr Stuart wanted. He knew, of course, he could not insult the hospital staff by refusing their kindness, so steeled himself to keep smiling for a while longer, as long as those precious parcels were put in the car for the homeward journey out of Pok-Fulam and back to Stanley Camp.

Dr Namura took Ennosuke to one side where they talked quietly for some minutes. Dr Namura then telephoned Tanaka which, Guy told Dr Stuart later, was to assure Tanaka that the visit was entirely satisfactory and Dr Ennosuke was proud to be of assistance to the Commandant, in his highly honoured but burdensome role!

Dr Namura was anxious to shepherd his charges back, Dr Stuart even more anxious to deliver his precious cargo safely home. But as Ennosuke was disappoined that the guided tour would not take place Namura relented to the extent of allowing a quick visit to the Irish lady. Only Rosie, Ennosuke and Dr Stuart went to see the patient. It was a familiar large, airy room with a lovely view of the tranquil sea, and the gardens. To Dr Stuart's bewildering surprise the King Pin was also visiting. He greeted them with a friendly smile, saying that the patient was a friend of his. The lady was full of admiration for the hospital and her treatment. She was happy to hear from her friend that people in camp were on the whole fit and coping with their internment. Life outside was hard, but the Japanese were doing all they could to look after the population.

The King Pin said his goodbyes and get-well-soons to the Irish lady, leaving with a curt nod to the three visitors. After a further few minutes, while Dr Stuart desperately shied off any queries on camp life, Ennosuke bowing slightly to the patient, ushered them out.

The car was waiting. There was a small parcel on Rosie's desk which she asked permission from Ennosuke to give to Dr Stuart. It contained, she said, some Chinese sweets for the camp patients and children. Ennosuke had a cursory look through the open flap and nodded his agreement. The farewells over, with a touching expression of gratitude from Dr Stuart, the car drove off, followed by the escort. During the journey back both Dr Stuart and Guy were eloquent in their praise for Dr Ennosuke and his staff. Dr Stuart happy now, watched the passing of the scenery he remembered with affection. Miyake, too, was busy translating Namura's observations and expressions of pleasure that the visit had been conducted for the assistance which Dr Stuart was so badly in need of to keep the hospital running smoothly. With the return to camp, even though there may be darker days ahead, Dr Stuart felt filled with a deep sense of peace. He had no idea of the hour, but the strange quietness and lack of bustle could only mean it was meal time! There were the preliminaries to go through with Tanaka and Dr Namura, who would give his report. The cartons were given to three internees sent for by Tanaka after Namura's telephone call from Pok-Fulam. The President was also there to welcome them back, telling Tanaka that the whole camp joined in his profound thanks for the great humanitarian act for which Tanaka had been responsible. Dr Stuart assured Tanaka that inoculation centres would be set up in the camp as early as possible the following morning. Dr Namura offered to send what members of his medical staff he could spare from the village centres. The offer was gratefully accepted should Dr Stuart find his staff could not cope.

The camp contingent were dismissed. The hospital was the first destination, the carefully packed vaccine to be safely stored in the hospital's only luxury, a splendid refrigerator. Plans for the next day were fixed and the equipment made ready for the most convenient areas.

During that day the camp seemed to function through an undercurrent of suspense. The blunt announcement of the suspected case of cholera was accepted philosophically. Notices were posted as to the assembly points for inoculation.

None of us had seen Peg at all. Her room-mate came into the library to tell me that she had caught a chill, so was wrapped up in bed sleeping most of the time. The only glimpse of Tom was when he went to the office just before curfew. This was to be reassured by the Senior Sister that Jan had been given a tetanus shot, his wounds stitched up, and a sedative administered. He had watched the return of the men from headquarters, carrying their loads as they headed for the hospital with Dr Stuart. Guy had gone briskly back to his own quarters.

There would be another long night's vigil for Tom and the boys, watching for a signal from the junk. Tom dearly wanted to try a personal contact in the early hours of the morning, but the boys finally convinced him that this was unthinkable. The Japanese were in an uneasy state; there were constant visits to our office by Miyake, and the risk of upsetting an already tenuous situation would be followed by an enormity of wrath unleashed on the whole camp and involving too many innocents.

As the evening darkened into night, the lights dancing on the calm bay, the normal chorus of yapping dogs and hum of the camp lent an aura of well-being. The hospital seemed more brightly lit up than usual. Tony told Rick that a staff car had come up the road later with two uniformed officers who were joined by the President and headed for the hospital. Tony had hoped to have a word with one of the hospital orderlies who had been in the carton-carrying party, but none of the three had as yet emerged from the hospital. No doubt plans were being made for tomorrow.

We teased each other as to who would get the first blunt needle. 'Very funny,' said Janie, 'but less funny than retching with cholera.' It seemed that each time someone tried to toss a light remark into the conversation, it turned into a hollow joke. The secret that Jan was the patient was blown wide open. The bearable phrase to cling to was 'Suspected Case'. Peg's fleeting references regarding Jan and something going on, were clouding my thoughts. Could there be any connection with the unusual liaison between the camp office and Up-The-Hill, which had gone on through the day? No contact with Peg or Joyce, no cheery meeting on the beach with Tom or Sid. There were definitely unspoken questions in both Tony and Rick's behaviour, as they walked off down the corridor together. Janie and I said goodnight on the way to our rooms.

'You're early, come and have a mug of tea.'

'Our arms are going to feel as if a pile driver had been working on them this time tomorrow,' Mother uttered gloomily having helped with vegetable cutting. We sat around, sometimes restlessly going to the balcony to look at the hospital. There was an unexplained feeling that a piece of the puzzle was missing in the day's events – our contacts were behaving mysteriously. We would have to wait for an explanation to dispense with the present inexorable feeling of danger looming round the corner.

The next day the inoculation centre was set up, hospital volunteers assisting the doctor at each of the areas. The hospital staff had had their jabs the night before. First to be done in camp were the kitchen staff's and Dutch quarters. There was a minimum of guards on display, no roll-call. The Japanese were being attended to by their own medicos Up-The-Hill. Everything went off in an orderly fashion, even the needles were sharp! People, rubbing their arms, compared notes as to the skill of their 'jabber' and took off for the waiting chores. A lighter atmosphere buoyed up the whole camp; the oppression of the day before had run out of steam.

Suki suggested we go and see Peg, who had been excused her jab for the time being, as she was feverish and full of headache. We fussed around her, collected her rations and left, promising to be back later. Her room-mate was on hospital duty, so she could rest quietly. We tried to find Tom, but he was off on

222

some camp chore. Suki was due at the maternity ward after her jab, and said miserably she hoped the Japanese medicos had left.

Before going to the library I watched the boat people going ashore in small numbers, realised that the village too would be having their inoculations. The large junk, leader of the fleet, was festooned with washing out to dry on bamboo poles, a small sampan tied up alongside.

Only the principals concerned with Jan's true condition knew that tonight held the destiny of so many souls in the balance. The frantic plans and decisions of the past two days would be weighed, won or lost by the coming dawn.

The bamboo pole of washing on the leader junk had given Tom a faint breathing space. He and Sid had been on alternative watch, concentrating on any change on the washing line, and towards early evening they had both confirmed that a red garment had been added to the end of the pole facing nearest the camp. The prayers to the Goddess of Mercy would be answered, one way or another, in the first clear light of morning.

Tom had promised Peg, who would also be watching and praying through that long night, from her doorway overlooking the bay, that at the sign of victory he would throw a beam from the torch in her direction. They saw the sampans ferrying the people back to their homes, the smoke from the cooking pots, the washing being collected off the lines. The red garment on the junk's pole was removed, and left draped on the hatch of the forward cabin. The darkness came, studded with a few boat lights. The leader junk showed a faint gleam from the topmast. More hours to fret in agony. The sleeping camp was

223

silent. Only a dim light could be seen from the office. The familiar sounds of the guards on duty drifted through the air as Tom and Sid drank endless mugs of warm tea.

Hope and despair took their toll. They had given up whispered encouragement to each other, locked in their private Gethsemane.

The sky was beginning to fill with the shades of dawn. There was a stirring in the bay, the leader junk sharply etched in a rosy pink. Tom and Sid, muscles bunched with cramp, stared with aching eyes for the signal. As the morning burst upon the bay, a proud green banner, the banner of the fleet, broke from the stern of the junk, and with her magnificent rust-coloured sails slowly billowing, her master at the helm, she majestically started voyage for the deep sea fishing waters. The final life-giving sound was the happy barking of her dog.

The message was received. Tom and Sid hugged each other in a vice. The torch beam flashed across to Peg. That must have been one of the most beautiful beginnings to any day! The miracle message from the master of the junk, the jubilation as great amongst the fleet and our little band who were concerned with the case. The colours of the dawn burst into daylight over the rippling sea, and the sky getting ready to gather up the heat of the sun was breathtaking. A reckless carnival mood caught the camp, and somehow we all knew that a crisis had been overcome. There were church services that evening by both denominations, giving thanks for the advent of summer, and deliverance from what could have been a disaster.

Much earlier that day Tom reported to the office. Emotions were high. Dr Stuart arrived with the Head

Sister. Tom was asked to tell them both the all clear had been given. The deception had miraculously worked. Tom left while Dr Stuart explained his strategy for diffusing the 'suspected' cholera case time bomb. Before Tom left, the doctor told him that Jan's anti-rabies treatment would continue its full course.

As the days went by there was jubilation throughout the Peninsula. The frightening prospect of an epidemic was over. Grumbles over sore arms continued, mostly to hide the stark relief. It was only on the morning it was learned that Dr Namura was visiting, and wished to see Dr Stuart, that Tom remembered the King Pin had been in the car that had followed Dr Stuart and his party to the main hospital. The first time he was allowed to visit a very wan-looking Jan, he asked Dr Stuart if he had seen the King Pin at all at the hospital. Dr Stuart told Tom of his call on the Irish lady, and surprise at seeing the King Pin in her room. When the turmoil had died down, Dr Stuart received a securely wrapped parcel with no reference to the donor. It contained a batch of local anaesthetics for the hospital's use. The doctor added that the camp dentist had got a similar package, much to his bewilderment and delight. Rumour, our daily newspaper, spread the word that the Blacks were subsidising the hospital drug racket! Both Dr Stuart and Toothy had a pretty good notion as to the donor of the very welcome gift – the King Pin was not all black-hearted. He was well aware too, Dr Stuart was sure, that the ride to Queen Mary Hospital had a special reason, not only for a stocking up of drugs. This, of course, was only confided to his colleagues.

# 13

Great news – a wedding was being planned! Josie said that she and Derek had agreed to take the matchmaker's advice. Derek had a small room off the club, which he shared with a chum, who said he was moving out as he couldn't stand the sight of the lovesick suitor when he had to leave his Josie. So great ideas for a really beautiful wedding got into top gear.

The kitchen staff, forever ready for the challenge of an occasion to show their art, happily agreed to provide the reception given the extras. Fortunately, we had another issue of Red Cross parcels, the fifth, so that would give the chefs plenty of encouragement! Suki rounded up two of the young to be decked out as flower girls. None of the boys would co-operate as page boys, so that idea was abandoned. Joyce was to be matron of honour, and we figured that would complete the wedding group.

Arrangements took up hours of our time. Paper had to be found for lists of guests, the menu, the garment for the wedding dress, flowers from the bushes, endless details! Rick elected to give the bride away, Tony to be the best man. Our camp 'jeweller' fashioned the ring out of a Hong Kong ten cent piece that Josie happened to have among her souvenirs.

In the meantime Jan was discharged from hospital,

very much thinner, but mentally his happy young self. He had been provided with a couple of elbow-length sleeved shirts, which successfully hid his ugly scars. He had also been encouraged not to try any strenuous exercise like underwater swimming! We all spoiled him. We knew instinctively that the long weeks he had been out of camp life had been perilous. Only the few knew how near to death he had been. His first social function would be the wedding, which drew closer, causing spasms of pessimism in case some important detail had been overlooked.

The padre had agreed to hold the ceremony in the club after the morning meal, which would give us all time to set things up. The day was set for the following Sunday, just four days to go. Josie was in a state of vapours.

All the arrangements were well in hand. The flowers for the bride and bridesmaids had to be left for the early morning of the Great Day, and the volunteers promised to get up at first light to scour the surroundings for what was available for the necessary bouquets, etc. Peg was in charge of helping the chef's catering, and setting out of the wedding brunch. Such cutlery and crockery as we could scrounge on loan was my job. Joyce and Suki would be dressing the bridal party. The lads obviously had some insane idea for the departure, which they spent a lot of time giggling over. We had never seen Tom and his cohorts in such a festive mood.

The unexpected came literally out of the blue. Two mornings before the Great Day, a joyful thunder of heavy aircraft was heard nearing the camp. As they appeared to pass overhead, the heavens rained down silver strips of what seemed to be aluminium, about a foot long. They fluttered slowly down through a cloudless sky like Christmas streamers. There was a mad rush all over the camp to collect them as they landed. This was a wonderful omen for the wedding, we all laughed, examining pieces gathered up from our section.

An immediate order came down from Tanaka. All internees to return to their quarters, and hand over any of the strips collected to their blockheads. There was a mercurial change in the mood of our captors. Guards were reinforced, and were noticeably hostile. No one was to be allowed to leave their immediate area until further notice.

That evening after the meal we got together in huddles of curiosity, trying to fathom the mystery of the silver rain. Everyone had a theory. Rick looked wise, but remained silent. There was no way of joining our chums, Joyce, Peg, all the others out of our area. We were in a fever of excitement, longing to exchange ideas as to what this new omen might mean. The guards were thick underfoot and in a mean mood. It would be hopeless to break the rules in this unexpected 'manna from heaven' situation. As ever optimistic, all agreed the silver rain had to be a message of hope.

Down in Tom's room, while the boys were waiting for a whisper of news on the latest visit from the air, Jan told Tom he had remembered the message given him by the junk master. 'There will be silver rain shortly, bringing good news!' They would have to wait for the junk's return, when a further message might be left near the beach.

All clear for fraternisation was given at roll-call the next day. The guards were still nervy and hostile. Derek and Josie were in a spin about Sunday, but arrangements were still going ahead amongst the organisers. The far off but unmistakeable drone of aircraft once again could be heard. Word went round in a matter of minutes; back to quarters for everyone. They came, showering Peninsula with the silver rain. This time only the guards were seen gathering up the strips. In the bungalow area they were able to salvage quite a few pieces before a posse of guards arrived to ensure no one was outside. The droning disappeared over the hills.

When the queues were formed for the morning meal Phil, the senior blockhead, called for attention, and read out the orders from Up-The-Hill:

'Only essential workers will be allowed to their details!'

'No group gatherings or social functions to be held.'

'Schools to close.'

'The beach to be closed.'

'All internees to remain in their own areas.'

The groans reverberated all through the camp, punctuated by optimistic hopes that the war news must be in the Allies' favour.

So that put paid to the Sunday wedding. The postponement was a bitter disappointment. No one could be sure when the restrictions would be lifted. Our committee asked that the orders given be strictly obeyed. No provocation by us would be tolerated. Tanaka was in an ugly mood again, and the present situation trying, but we must understand and obey.

Fortunately none of the edibles had been prepared, and the rest of the plans had to be put on hold. Poor Josie and Derek – they, like ourselves, were plagued by whether to be optimistic that it augured great news, or unhappy for the prospective bridal couple.

After all they could have their marriage ceremony without all our exciting brouhaha on Sunday. The Rev. Rose of the Church of England was in the building, and we were sure he would take the ceremony with those of us present, if the couple really wanted it.

That evening the camp was enveloped in a brooding hush. Even the young ones were less noisy and exuberant. None of us could settle down to the usual Saturday night bridge sessions or play readings. We got round in our favourite groups and the future was seriously discussed, sometimes with trepidation.

After a short sleepless night for many of us, Sunday opened the day with a grey face, and a light drizzle of tears. The ration lorries were late. The gangs of kitchen workers could be seen waiting around to collect the rations, otherwise there were only the drab uniforms worn by the guards, plodding damply to relieve their mates. The sun blundered through a couple of times with the promise of a brighter afternoon. All ears were tuned for the now expected rumble of aircraft.

There was no rumble. No silver rain. No lifted restrictions. The sun did appear, drying up the soggy surroundings. The restless children were unleashed to chase each other round the courtyard. Clothing and bedding began to be seen out of windows on the balconies for airing. The sea beyond us was empty of craft. The fisherfolks' haven in the bay too, was unnaturally void of movement.

The padre, who was in one of our blocks, as was Josie, visited Rick to tell him that he advised any celebrations be cancelled. When the camp returned to normal there was to be a quiet ceremony, with no reception to follow. Although we all realised the need for caution, it was a dreary finale to something that had not even begun.

This curtailment of movement was reminiscent of being caged in the Chinese hotels prior to camp. At least there were no rats to eat our soap, for those who still had some! The beach outings were missed most of all. The library gatherings to gossip, meet and discuss would return, but perhaps not our beach outings – it would be too difficult to round us up.

Monday came and the hospital volunteers were allowed back on duty. The day passed in boredom, with only the chores to break the wait for the chow queue. No further air activity. On Tuesday, with duties piling up, more of us were released to get on with things, until by Wednesday the camp was allowed to crawl back to life. The schools were opened, but the bitter pill was that the beach was still banned, as we had suspected.

The mood of the camp was lethargy – everyone seemed to be dragging their feet with nothing but dreary chores to cope with. We prayed that the big bomb boys would return with their silver rain – but the skies were as sullen and non-communicative as all of us.

On Saturday a musical evening was to be held in St Stephens. Derek and Josie, at the suggestion of the padre, would be married with just five of us present. The only celebration would be the cutting of the magnificent cake the kitchen staff went ahead and made. This would take place in Derek's small room. A toast by courtesy of Tom, in a loving cup of his vintage rice wine. Then we would be off to the singsong.

It was a gay little attendance, the padre reminding us of unknown events ahead, when the Good Lord would be at our side. We drank another toast to that too! We were all feeling sentimental, nostalgic and slightly high as we left the couple, winding our way to the lusty singing and cheerful piano concertos of our musical colleagues.

Tom's junk had been back and out several times since the cholera 'scare' but no message was left near the beach. Now that contact with the beach was cut Peg pleaded for no alternative action. The nightmare of those forty eight hours still preyed on her mind. She had got even thinner, very moody and withdrawn. We worried, but felt it was better not to jolly her along. Once the beach was opened up, which it surely must be, she would snap out of her malaise.

We naturally did not know what secret plan had been thought out to contact the junk master – but there was general disappointment that no theories were forthcoming from our colleagues for the reason for the silver rain. The powers that be had obviously been alerted as to its meaning whilst the rest of us had no idea what it represented.

The overall physical state of the internees at the camp was deteriorating noticeably amongst the older people. Mei reported confidentially that the Blacks were running very short of supplies. As Rick pointed out this was a good sign as obviously shipping was having difficulty in bringing in their cargo. Cases of beri-beri reappeared, and patients were not responding to treatment as rapidly as in the earlier days.

The more erudite citizens began discussing the outcome of the final days. For the rest, we ploughed on through bursts of despondency versus optimism. Soon the summer would be over and there would be another dreary Arctic winter to struggle with. The comfort of our monthly postcards continued being sent and received. Although the messages were fairly stereotyped, there was the illusion of being in touch with others outside the confines of the camp.

We had been given advance notice that there was a possibility of sending a small gift to our families across the harbour this coming Christmas! Old Baldy-Balls-Up, always ready to have a crack at the Blacks, said he had inside information that the Blacks had spread this advance notice to encourage their dwindling sales! However, it was a new topic for brain-wracking. Endless ideas were swapped and discarded. Alex, our Russian teacher cum artist, said he would gladly paint a portrait of my head and shoulders from the one precious wedding postcard I had managed to rescue.

'Aha, but I have no canvas, my little friend, we must give this great thought.'

Alex was in one of his frequent defeatist periods. However, there was still time for the inventive Tony to come up with the solution.

As the burning hot days dragged by, with no relief from cooling off in that clean clear blue-green sea, the walk via Siberia became more deserted during the still evenings. The real attraction was to get to the point from which we could see Stanley main road curving round the hill, sit watching the magical colours of the flame trees and bauhenias vying with the sun's violent sky-painting while setting. The great balloon of deep scarlet was slowly lowering herself to meet the now golden sea and the nostalgia caught one's throat as if in a vice. So many of the large trees in our surrounds had been sacrificed for cooking fuel. One small bauhenia tree at the exit of the cemetery usually managed to deck herself out with her mauve bllooms. St Stephen's and the bungalow areas still had a semblance of gardens where hibiscus bushes cheered up the residents and visitors. Sadly, green lawns were missing, but the hillside shrubs managed to dress up in their spring greens each season.

The beach ban was suddenly lifted! The atmosphere in camp changed to one of fiesta. The daily wash was gathered to be taken down to the beach, the bucket lines formed. The sound of the kids squealing, people calling out to each other, and the horseplay shouts from the sea drifted up to camp like a well-rehearsed orchestra. What bliss to relax even for a short spell, in that worry-free playpen.

Reports were coming from the bungalow dwellers that there was much troop movement along the main road to the garrison. Infantry and trucks were on the move both day and night. By tacit agreement, those of us who had no official reason for moving around that area kept well away, hoping to give the impression that no undue interest was being taken in the sudden development.

Tom was particularly interested in these movements. He had at long last been able to pick up the 'special' message. Coming back from a visit to the office he stopped by to see Rick, hinting that the outside news of the Allies was breathtaking. Unbeknown except to the vital few, D-Day had taken place.

There was no further silver rain, though distant gunfire, and still the high up thunder of aircraft could be heard intermittently. No word slipped out, but the ready smiles from Tom and the boys were more effective. Peg had snapped out of her dismal depths, confiding to us that the syndicate were definitely not planning anything more hairy-scary.

It was still very puzzling that there had been no great air activity for some time. It was crucial that the news from the junk master, which Tom had given the President, be kept under wraps as far as the camp was concerned. Tanaka might suspect news was leaking into us, but the game of cat and mouse had to be played by our two sides, certainly for the time being.

Before the beach days were over, heralding winter, an extraordinary rumour with unpleasant implications began the rounds. No one could imagine its source, it was so bizarre, but it was going through camp as rapidly as internal combustion.

Preparations were to be put in hand for tunnels to be dug into the surrounding hillsides. These were to act as air-raid shelters in the event of aerial attacks. They would be for the women and children only.

Squads of our men would be formed to make these shelters as quickly as possible. Next the women and children would be drilled in teams similar to lifeboat stations. Thus would the weaker sex be saved with their young. There was a howl of angry disbelief from the women. Obviously some wag had dreamed this one up to give us all something to argue about in the long cold winter evenings.

When we questioned Tom and Rick they just smiled and said to forget about it – some rumour had filtered in that the Philippines were moving their foreigners out of their camps and sending them up to makeshift accommodation in the hills. Perhaps this had been thought our solution in case of bombing?

Despite the persistence of the rumour, not even Ben was able to discover the source. Eventually discussions on this grim scenario for the camp were discouraged and the subject dropped. Every now and then, if one of our weaker sex should incur a male's

235

displeasure, she would be threatened by the 'sex tunnel' as the rumour became known!

End of another summer. More graves had been filled and more babies yelled their way into the unreal world of Stanley Camp. Preparations for yet another winter began to occupy our free time. The carpenters were busy patching up draughty windows and holes in the bungalows' leaking roofs, tailors patching and remaking winter garments, woodcutters laying in stocks for the kitchens. All of us husbanded what few stocks we had left of our Red Cross parcels for the colder days that brought the all too familiar hunger pangs.

The generous allowances from the POWs bought very much less from the Blacks, but even a couple of sticks of wong tong would help generate a bit of warmth. The Blacks had very limited stocks of food and cigarettes; hence the prices were astronomical. None of our allowances could afford more than a meagre stick of wong tong, or the odd duck egg between the three of us.

# 14

The outlook for Christmas was bleak. In fact most of us preferred to forget the so-called festive season. The entertainment committee was slogging hard to produce evenings of light relief, but it wasn't easy to find enthusiastic takers for the more energetic roles!

After much debating it was jokingly suggested that as most of the children were about the healthiest specimens in camp, perhaps the theme should be centred on them. The committee agreed that this was a splendid idea, especially as the main load of the work with the kids would be done by the indomitable Carol. Thus the Christmas ballet began. Several clever contributions for short skits involving the teenagers were accepted. The very young were to be regimented as background.

The star of the teenies was to be Blossom, aged four. She was an enchanting person, slightly bow-legged, slightly pot-bellied, slightly pigeon-toed. There was a short growth of almost silver down on her head, ending in a flourishing duck's tail on the nape of her neck! Her parents were a young couple who had come to Hong Kong from Canton, where her father had worked for one of the larger companies, just prior to our war. They were, of course, snarled up in the events, arriving with the rest of us at Stanley Camp. They were completely disenchanted with the world, and each other, and preferred to remain remote from the basics of camp life. The father was a sick man, so excused from any manual labour. He was tall, gangling, prematurely semi-bald with myopic eyes enlarged by steel-rimmed spectacles. He felt that it was his wife's affair to look after the child. His wife was an adult replica of Blossom, except that her platinum hair was long and thick. Her theory was that as long as approximately 2000 odd bodies were around, a few might be willing to attend to the child, and she could use her time better by attending all the lectures, joining the myriad of classes provided by competent members in our midst, while relief from the academics was chosen from personable males.

Thus Blossom became the child of the camp. She had complete freedom of choice in habits, and was a great favourite of the King Pin with whom she frequently dined! Billy, of course, monitored her movements as much as possible. He could be seen towing her away from St Stephen's at curfew time, back to quarters. She spoke fluent Japanese and Chinese. All the guards were under her spell. If she were around when they were going off duty, they would give her piggy-back rides as far as the guard quarters, from where she would solemnly pigeon-toe her way back to familiar ground.

It was planned that in the finale of the children's show Blossom would pop her way out of an enormous paper egg, suitably dressed as the New Year. When this was explained to her Blossom decided she would be very happy to oblige if she were allowed to sing 'Happy Birthday' to the audience. Right!

Arrangements were made for the show to be held

in early autumn, before the really cold weather started, a convenience to the children. As many of us as possible were corralled into helping with rehearsals and arrangements. A severe test of patience and humour! Most of the cast behaved like angels, the older ones keeping order amongst the rest.

Apart from the everyday frustrations the wheels were grinding along undramatically. The show was taking shape. The brown leaf smell of coming autumn wafted pleasantly over the camp. No one appeared to be brewing up for a hassle.

Suddenly the boom was lowered. All hell broke loose. For two days no one had seen Blossom. Her parents were the least knowledgeable about her social engagements. It had often happened that Blossom had spent a night with one of her many chums, so that they were quite unconcerned.

The committee decided that a thorough search of all her haunts be made before bringing the Japanese into the act. She couldn't be too far away.

The alert went out. Word came back from various areas as to where and when she had been seen last. The King Pin set his eyes and ears into action. The Blacks normally got any scuttle-butt that was going. The search was on.

It was Billy, a very unusually white-faced Billy, who got hold of Tom to tell him that one of the kids had seen Blossom playing round the ration lorry a couple of days before. Tom passed this along to the King Pin.

The following morning, as the ration lorries drew into camp, the King Pin was personally at the parking bay to question the drivers. There was no need. A demented driver deposited a self-possessed, if rather smelly and begrimed Blossom into his arms. He was almost sobbing with fright as he explained his dilemma.

It appeared that Blossom had been found on the driver's return to the depot, asleep surrounded by banana skins, in a heap of rotten vegetables which the cooks had refused to accept. The driver was beside himself with terror, as his next duty as ration driver was not until the day after he had found her. He was advised by his fellow drivers to take her home to his family, and deliver her back on his next tour. She had chatted away to them all in Chinese, delighted to be with them, saying that she spent lots of nights in other rooms without her Mummy and Daddy worrying.

The situation was traumatic. If reported officially the repercussions for the unfortunate driver could be devastating. So, in his great wisdom, and with his power at the top, the King Pin warned that as long as the silence of all those involved was assured, he would consider the matter closed.

Blossom was returned to the cast, her 'fairy tale' accepted and no questions asked. The children bedevilled her to tell them her adventure. Luckily Blossom concocted so many varying versions that in the excitement of the advancing show, curiosity was replaced by the importance of their own stage appearances. All personnel connected with rations were warned to beware of unauthorised persons lurking in the vicinity! We hardly even dared to think upon what could so easily have been the outcome of Blossom's lorry ride.

A reminder went out mid-November that all Christmas packages for the POW camps must be handed to our authorities by December 1.

Panic stations flared up. Was Alex still prepared to go ahead with his suggestion of my painting?

'Of course, my little friend, but we must find the canvas.'

Tony said he had been working on just the job, it would be ready the next day. It was a beautiful buffed piece of wood, 5½″ × 6½″.

'Perfect for oils, I have been experimenting myself.'

Tony was delighted to donate the wood for Alex's masterpiece.

That evening I took my postcard with the piece of wood to Alex, whose quarter was in St Stephens. He was a bit taken aback at the fact that now he would have to make a decision! The evening was perfect, cool in the fading sunset. Alex was at peace. My luck could be in. He examined Tony's handiwork with a connoisseur's eye.

'Tony is too clever, this is fine craftsmanship, it will be a pleasure to work on it.'

Producing a pretty little china cup of real China tea, he mused over the plaque. Itching to ask how long it would take, I steered away from the question. It could so easily bring on a deep depression! We skimmed over camp events, casually touching on the 'alleged disappearance' of young Blossom, the creative wonder of Carol, the splendour of the ballet. Then we got down to the nitty-gritty. Giving me a hug as I got up to go, his bright eyes dancing, he said, 'You shall call for the masterpiece on the thirtieth of this month.'

Tony promised to pack the gift carefully for me. Later I went to see Mei who, in her big-hearted fashion, assured me that she would have a small packet of real China tea for me to give Alex for his Christmas present. Not daring to ask how much I would need to pay for it, I hoped there would be enough left over from the allowance to get perhaps five fags for Tony. If desperate I knew Fred would finance me as this was a special, not to be repeated loan.

On November 30 Sukie and I found Alex on the front step, waiting to give me the precious gift. We were ecstatic. Alex was thrilled, warning me to treat it gently as it was not quite dry! We stayed a while to admire some of his work, both water colours and charcoal drawings. He roughly waved my stammering thanks away. The package had to be handed in to Phil to take to the office, at the latest by the next morning. Tony was lavish in his praise and set to work packing it. He had noticed that the paint was not absolutely dry, and didn't look very happy about the packaging. Nothing could stop my enthusiasm. Phil mentioned that the wrapping might be opened by the censor, Tanaka or whoever. So off it went with the other gifts, to the office Up-The-Hill.

Mother thought it was lovely but was sad there was not time to show it off to the rest of the gals. There was time, though, to make a quick visit to Peg and Joyce to let them know it was on its way. Knowing Alex's moods they had been a bit sceptical of it being ready on the required date.

The next visit was to Mei to collect the tea and fags, praying the cost would not cause me to faint away! Fred had already told me not to worry, he would look after anything surplus to what I was holding in my hot hand. Mei had both items wrapped in paper for me. From the small amount that Fred had to ante up I was morally sure Mei had smuggled them out of stock. She was truly a good friend.

The two parcels were stored away in a Red Cross carton to join the other gifts put aside for Christmas. That night my imagination went through the whole

242

gamut of how and when but never if we would all meet again – when being the operative question. This was to have been 'nineteen forty-four sigh no more!'

The weather had suddenly turned decidely chilly. We were glad to haul out the somewhat sad-looking winter woollies. The navy blue slacks vintage 1940, after many washings in sea water, were practically able to stand up by themselves! They still kept most of the draughts out, especially in the library when the club doors were continually being opened. Joyce and I were sorting books and discussing the surprise for the boys when their Christmas gifts arrived. Joyce had a younger brother who had been in the Royal Naval Volunteer Reserve. He was a big chap in every way, and she and Mama-T had sent him a tin of bully beef from their last Red Cross parcel, knowing how enormous his appetite had always been. Rice, said Joyce, he could eat a mountain of it at every sitting. We started planning our first Chinese chow after our release – a constant pastime which managed to titillate the taste buds for the morning meal, when Myra came up looking rather worried. Phil had asked her to let me know that he wanted to see me right away. A message from authority brought on the familiar feeling of ants crawling all over me. With a whispered 'Good luck' from Joyce, I started off for his room. There was absolutely nothing I could imagine he might wish to discuss. My feeling was rather that of being summoned to the head mistress's office, wondering which broken rule was to be answered for.

Phil was waiting for me in the corridor. Taking me firmly by the arm he said that I was wanted in the office. Before there was time to ask any questions we arrived to find the President, Guy and Miyake. They

243

all looked relaxed and unforbidding, but inside my board-stiff slacks the legs seemed to have lost all capability of movement. Neither did my head belong to my body as the mind went blank while some sort of explanation was being given me, or was I being asked for an explanation? The past but familiar ritual between Miyake, Tanaka and myself of a conversation about bridges which had overwhelmed me then, engulfed me now, as I tried to make the connection.

I must have looked quite moronic. Guy had put a stool behind me onto which he lowered me by the shoulders. The President, Guy and Miyake were talking across and around me, the conversation was unintelligible. Sure that nothing in that room that was happening was real, I wanted to get up and leave, but found that the legs still wouldn't function. There was a quiet period. Then Guy's soothing voice was telling me very calmly that he was to accompany me Up-The-Hill. All I could think of was Nan's shower-language, SPC!

Miyake moved to the door, as did Guy, steering me in front of him. We took the same route as before. The well-known faces smiled encouragingly as we passed. Ye Gods, what vile deed had I committed? Why had I not been able to understand why we were taking this awesome walk? *Think!*

If I had been chilly before, now frostbite had set in. This time only the guard was at the foot of the steps which, with Guy's strong hand in my back, I was able to negotiate. The same routine at the front door, entering the same room, with the large desk behind which was the same Tanaka. The identical words barked out. Then the order I knew was coming.

'Turn round.'

This had to be a recurring nightmare. It couldn't be really happening. Remembering this time to keep my eyes open, and trying to recall my answers as before, I turned.

Unbelievable. On the mantelpiece no postcard, but propped up against the wall the portrait Alex had done for my Christmas gift for David.

At this point Guy took over. I began to thaw. The atmosphere was like a genteel drawing-room tea party. Waiting for the punchline the senses cleared. Tanaka was once again lolling back in his chair, with cigarette. Miyake was actually showing his teeth, but not in anger, and Guy was patiently talking as if to a two-year-old, watching me try to assimilate the reason for my visit.

In simple language the good Commandant wished to tell me that this 'very handsome picture was still damp, would spoil if sent with the rest of the gifts to the POWs, and would therefore remain on the mantelpiece until dry enough to repack and send to the Argyle Street POW camp.

It therefore followed that the gift would be late in arriving, but I was to understand that it would be sent.

I found myself giving my salutation of bows, too confused to utter my gratitude, remaining in a daze whilst Guy exchanged pleasantries with Tanaka. The next move came in slow motion, as bowing again, Guy and I went through the front door and down the steps. I was surprised to see it was still daylight. The visit surely must have lasted far into the night.

Both Phil and Joyce were waiting in the office when we walked in. Or rather Guy walked, I reeled into the nearest chair, automatically taking the mug Joyce was holding out to me.

Guy gave a detailed description of the interview. There was simply no way of figuring out the object of the visit. By the haste with which Phil, Joyce and I were hurried out, it did occur to Phil that Guy and the President had motives for discussion. It was incomprehensible that the Great Man was actually doing me a favour or that he was an art buff or even that the ghost of the colonel's wife was still pursuing me; 'Ladies all . . .' Could he have some fiendish trick to haunt me with? Would I ever know the answer? Perhaps he was genuine in his concern for the safe arrival of the gift. I was delirious to be safely back on familiar ground, hoped fervently there would not be a third time on that particular ground. Poor Mother spent a long time worrying about her ewe lamb, and begging me to keep as close as possible to Block No. 4.

Mother was being kept company by Janie. After hearing my very lame sounding story Mother pshawed, 'Such chivalry from THAT one. Just wait till Churchill hears about it! Scaring the stays off us all, and then with his fancy talk!'

The rest of the day was spent listening to comforting remarks like, 'Third time lucky!' The news of my visit Up-The-Hill reached Alex.

Poor Alex was in a state of collapse, being quite sure that the Japanese suspected secret notes printed into the portrait. The tea soothed him. Tony insisted that his much appreciated fags would be held back for THE special news which, he predicted, was not too far away. Alex muttered gloomily that they would probably disintegrate by the time Tony still had breath to draw on them.

New Year rolled in to 'forty-five we're still alive' – uttered on a surprised note. A slight upheaval was very evident at the top. There were changes in the guards, making identification difficult. Humpty Dumpty, to everyone's regret, was replaced by an evil-looking Formosan, who saw to it that he was taking no nonsense from the kids. No handouts, no smiles. The kids finally gave up wasting their time trying to charm the bastard, taking their defeat out on each other!

Miyake, too, had been replaced. I came in for a lot of teasing as to when I would first require his replacement's interpretation. Happy thoughts. There was a definite slackness in the regime. Roll-calls were often called off and fraternisation after curfew was not nearly so hazardous. Tony put this down to the weather. The winter was certainly adding to the general discomfort, lack of body-heating meals, and rather tired winter clothing. People tended to stay closer to home, when possible. The evening concerts were not quite so heavily attended. Replacements were more frequently required for manual labour, as flu, roaring colds and coughs swept through the outdoor workers.

Even the rumour-mongers had gone to ground, making the evening get-togethers less interesting. Tempers were easily touched off the handle. The blockheads preached brotherly love as more disputes came to them for settlement. Changes of accommodation were pleaded for as vendettas amongst room-mates grew in ridiculous proportion to the situation.

Many moons had passed since the last Red Cross parcel, six had been distributed so far; another handout would certainly inject a cheerful diversion. Most of us were back to relying solely on the camp rations. Quite a number of the Blacks' customers moaned that their choice of luxuries was limited. No more fruit was coming in to spend the allowances on. Life truly presented a disheartening picture.

As though by collective thought-transference the parcels arrived. The allocation was to be one and a half parcels per person! The gloomers were certain this odd number meant the last delivery. News of wild shipping losses to the Japanese fleet, sweeping victories in the Pacific, supported the theory, and also brought a shaking off of the apathy which had bogged us down. The parcels were hugged with joy, but there was a little more caution about having a celebration party. The contents were devoured less greedily, there was a little more careful putting away for that kill-joy, the rainy day. A label from one of the tins received in St Stephens Quarters was left in the library for anyone to read. Printed in block capitals, beneath the contents was the sentence, 'WE ARE ALL THINKING OF YOU, HAVE HEART'.

Some miserable creatures insisted that it was not genuine, but most of us preferred to believe it was.

Spring was fluttering coyly round the corner. Bounce and banter infected the depression, as camp cries and rumours flooded over the dreary routine. This splintered unexpectedly as the first line of ration lorries lumbered down the road. It was a perfect, clear, sun-drenched spring morning. Over the hills dividing Stanley Peninsula from the Island we could hear muffled sounds of bombs, and concentrating one's eyes on the sky, roughly over Kowloon, the mainland, objects droning like hungry mosquitoes were darting and diving in and out of range. We knew the drill by now. Waiting until the droning was closer before we trudged back to quarters, the thumbs-up sign could be seen as we passed each other.

In a matter of minutes, from nowhere and everywhere, these wonderful machines buzzed round the camp, like friendly puppies wagging their tails. We were screaming and waving from windows and balconies. Quite a few of our men could be seen outside the buildings, flailing their arms like windmills. The aircraft made another pass across the camp, much lower, tipping their wings, and then off to the garrison on the hill where we could hear the rattle of machine-guns before flying away.

Far, far too soon the only noise was the excited babble of the community. It was the most exhilarating experience we had ever had. The hell with the cost in restriction of movement, etc. We could all swear that we had actually seen the faces of the pilots wondering how much damage they had been able to inflict on the garrison. We would soon know, as the mayhem would be measured by the punishment meted out!

This time there had been no anti-aircraft guns sounding off. Some windows around the camp had been cracked by the low buzzing, which became the camp tourist attraction.

As our soaring spirits came down to earth, we started tentatively moving about in the open, traipsing back to the job that had been so gloriously interrupted. The day wore on, still without orders as to a change in the daily pattern. It was difficult to control our boisterous feelings, but we all knew we were treading dangerously.

The evening notice board made a brief reference to 'a slight intrusion, of enemy (!) aircraft, successfully repelled'. Our blockheads quietly asked us to refrain from any unusual activities, and keep our evening gatherings small and sober! The Japanese could be planning some trick to give them an excuse for reprisals. We were models of subdued captives, retiring to our baliwicks long before curfew! But what orgies we planned in the ghettos for that night! Breaking into the Red Cross parcels' hard rations, brewing up mugs of tea, and tirelessly going over every moment of the 'raid'. Phil told Rick that he would be wise to organise the block's lookout for the night. There could be a late surprise room check. The night passed without a visitation but watching eyes noted that Up-The-Hill lights were shining strongly, while more than one car had been spotted arriving at Tanaka's headquarters.

The activity Up-The-Hill continued for several nights. Something significant had to be afoot. The bulletin board had little to report – one or two domestic items of little interest. Our committee appeared to be keeping very much under cover. Neither Tom nor Joyce were very chatty, making it difficult to ask them 'What goes on?'

For the next few days, news leaked in that there had been injuries in the POW camps, but nothing fatal, thank God! Certain Japanese troop lines had been hit, with fairly heavy casualities. Splendid! Although we were so thankful there were no fatalities within the POW camps, it was a harrowing thought that reprisals, perhaps brutal ones, might be meted out to our men. It was untenable that we could be so close, measured as the proverbial crow flies, and get hardly any news that could be authenticated.

The daylight raids continued away over the hills, and though we all prayed for another 'raid' on us, it never came. Reluctantly we settled back into the monotony. However, most nights a steady whine of aircraft high above us could be heard. The camp was bubbling under the surface, a forced nonchalance hiding the obvious anxiety in our male colleagues.

Slowly the old order was re-established. Peg had met Mei one morning on their way to the library. There was trouble afoot with the King Pin. The news had been kept under wraps, but two nights before there had been an unaccountable raid on the Blacks' main storage godown. This godown was kept very close to Japanese headquarters, usually guarded.

Quite a number of expensive essentials had been rifled. So far there was no hint as to how or by whom. Mei said that it was undoubtedly the work of experts. More than the loss of the goods was the loss of face for the King Pin. He had promoted a 'seek and find' operation, which boded bad trouble if the operation were to bear fruit. Peg was terribly disturbed. She had a shrewd idea that Tom's syndicate could be involved. Life had been uneventful for them far too long.

There was an uneasy feeling that people were being watched, others pumped for information. The Blacks were edgy. Trading had stopped, it was rumoured, until the culprits and/or the goods were found.

The King Pin could, and was, making life fairly unpleasant. Word went out that if the goods were returned to any of the Blacks' trading posts, all would be forgiven. If not, consequences would be dire.

Rations in some areas became short for a couple of days. One or two of the guards began patrolling around the kitchens whilst the meals were being prepared. Sid and one of the other boys in the syndicate were ambushed one night returning from a poker game out of their area. They were roughly manhandled, sporting a black eye or two and badly scraped knuckles between them. Still there was no information whatsoever on the culprits.

The whole camp was becoming embroiled, and the situation was becoming ugly. Mei told Peg some weeks later that the President had called a meeting of the committee asking the King Pin to attend. Mei did not reveal exactly what had taken place, but apparently honour was satisfied, Tom's guess being momentarily satisfied. The dogs were called off.

# 15

Beach days made their debut once more. For the opening season of our little group, Tom and the boys arranged a picnic. No rations to be allowed, only guests! We gathered together on the rocks within the beach boundary. After a cooling off in the inviting sea, Tom called 'chow down'. What a mouth-watering feast! As we ate long forgotten delicacies like tinned sausages, sardines and fruit, the mystery of the raided godown was solved! We learned after the party that the bulk of the goods had been for the hospital, which was very short of nourishing menus for the convalescents. Every mouthful was savoured, even more so when we learned the truth. No questions were allowed to be asked, our mouths were naturally assumed to be zipped up. They were!

Suki said to me that evening that she had wondered where the half of tinned peach Florrie was enjoying, after a painful mastectomy, had come from. As the hospital was never discussed outside, she had not thought to mention it to me before.

The only reference Tom ever made to the consequences of the raid, was that the King Pin had made a tactical error by recruiting the Japanese to poke their noses in.

There was a new interpreter, Yamashita, who spent

a lot of time around the camp, also with the committee. Many of the old hands recognised him as the owner of the barber shop in the Hong Kong Hotel before the war! Rick felt it was significant that he had replaced Miyake. He would not, however, expand on the significance.

The fleet in the bay had shrunk, and the master junk had not been in for longer than we could remember. The lovely summer evenings were uncannily quiet without the boat-dog chorus that would go on far into the night. We missed the friendly winking lights of the sampans which were also absent. Watching the depleted hubbub amongst the fisherfolk as they visited the beach and each other left a lonely, disturbing feeling.

There was an uncomfortable spell of torrential rain, making a continual battle against mildew, as it was difficult to air one's clothing. More important was not being able to collect the small amounts of fire-fuel for our individual chatties. With the hot steamy days and nights, that welcome hot mug was still the greatest panacea.

Joyce got a message to me that a bale-out job needed to be done in the library. Getting down as early as possible the next morning, with a bit of old sacking Bottom of the kitchen staff had given me, I indeed found the library floor was afloat. Joyce had also managed to wheedle a couple of old sacks from somewhere, so with the help of Billy, plus a rather battered tin can, we set to work. The hall was empty; it was too damp for early morning activities. While the three of us were mopping up as best we could, Joyce whispered that she had a package for me. When most of the deluge had been squeezed out, and Billy went off on other business, Joyce produced a bundle of chopped wood. She explained smugly that, during the vandalisation of the library floor, she had managed to secrete a couple of squares of parquet away, half of which I was entitled to, and this was the time to use it. One of the boys had splintered the wood for her, and I was given my share. Manna!

Dodging back to the room, my precious cargo tucked under my flour bag blouse, I found only mother. She was squatting over the chattie, near the balcony, trying disconsolately to fan some tired-looking leaf mould into action. The wood disgorged from my garment, Mother set to work. Just a few pieces were needed to get a glow up, and the pot was on the hob. As the others trooped in, squelching uncomfortably, they were handed the healing potion to sip contentedly before the next task.

Having delivered the precious parquet slivers to Mother – gulping down a welcome mouthful of the nectar, I went off back to the library. On my way I saw the back of a bedraggled figure, heading my way too. It was Suki. She must have been coming off early morning hospital duty. We met at the library where I was relieving Joyce; not many people were venturing out, so the room was practically empty. When Suki saw me she sat on the window sill and, covering her tired little face with her hands, began to sob quietly. I was about to try and comfort her, asking what had upset her but Joyce wisely said to leave her to slowly calm down.

The room started to fill up with some of the old lags coming in to air the latest gossip. Suki seemed to have controlled her outburst and joined me behind the bar. The last hospital shift she had been on was a terrible shock to her. She had been asked by one of the nurses to help with a maternity case, as the wards were just getting ready for their rice-gruel breakfast. She had felt quite honoured, as it was the first time she had helped at any real event. But it was not what any young trainee would be excited about – it was an abortion. She managed to keep down her nausea, but what had really shaken her was that most of us knew the lady undergoing this unnatural experience, and that her husband was a POW in the officer's camp in Kowloon. The nurse had registered Suki's dismay and had taken her to one side, making her promise not to mention anything to anyone – and with a further bout of tears she had promptly told me. This, and the fact that the nurse, who was one of the senior professionals, had said that this was not the first, nor she suspected would be the last such operation to be performed; after all, she said to Suki, we were living in very non-conventional times! A good summing up, we thought.

Outside news was being received thick and fast by our authorities. Obviously none of this could be spread universally. Some stupendous events were whispered to responsible persons. These in turn, reached the rest as 'reliable' rumours: the recapture of the Philippines, 'VE Day'. Most of them were dismissed as wishful thinking. Nevertheless an aura of confidence began to steal into our discussions regarding these momentous happenings. Certainly the men we knew and trusted were less inclined to pooh-pooh the rumours as rubbish. One did notice, however, that there was a mood of uncertainty about them, discouraging premature jubilation.

Whenever we could, we would go over the same old ground. In what form would the end of the war come? Again the camp was divided by the happy-go-luckies – 'Oh you'll see, everything will be fine' – and

256

the doom-predictors – 'The bastards will machine-gun the lot of us.' Charming! The more middle of the road lot were unshaken in their faith that our authorities had the ultimate plan for most eventualities. After all, the Chinese people, and the Chinese Army too, no doubt, would be on hand.

It was noticeable that the guards were not quite so vigilant. Particularly the beach team. It was not unusual for the pillbox to be unmanned. Once the beach was open for use a couple of bored guards watched the lines of beach-goers on their way down, but they rarely bothered to man the approach during the times allowed us away from the main area. There was hardly any fear of attempted escapes. Most of the ambulatory bodies were too undernourished to think about escape; in the final analysis there was nowhere to go anyway, especially with the shark warning. You had to be pretty intrepid to risk a swim across the bay, even if you could have made it.

Towards the height of the season we found that after the evening meal there didn't seem to be any objection to bucket-lines for a last fill up, which meant that if we didn't abuse the extended hour or so, we could have a quick refreshing dip after chores. Our authorities were not quite so happy about the assumption that small groups could take advantage of the new order, so made it loud and clear that it was not to be a daily occurrence. The ever volatile mood Up-The-Hill could change, making a nasty issue of these quick trips.

Very few of us women were welcome. The men felt in the event of an incident we would be a liability. Rightly so, but some of us did join the bucket lines on the odd evening.

It was on one of these evenings that a party filling

257

their buckets got a warning call of 'Shark sighted'. This was the first time a shark had actually been in close enough to be recognised. A quick retreat up the beach ended any ideas of a refreshing dip. Phil was afraid this sighting might result in curtailment of the frequent use of the sea which, of course, would have a deeply depressing affect on our morale. Perhaps Tanaka would turn a deaf ear to any 'no beach' suggestions. Phil was not usually given to morbid speculations. We wondered if he had heard anything on the bamboo wireless.

Arriving for hospital duty that same night, I told the story to Buck, one of the orderlies. How was it that sharks were invading our bay, when they had never been in these waters before the war? Buck said roughly that I must be very naive. Many junks had been machine-gunned off our bay, and certainly numbers of dead men from the jail had been dumped in the sea around us. Less trouble than burials. Jesus, how macabre, but it sounded feasible.

Buck was in a chatty mood, and told me of the terrific response the hospital had had when blood transfusions had been required, and the ceaseless efforts by the medical staff to save their patients, with so little to work with. He was unshakeable in his belief that the Pacific war was in the final stage, that the misery would be over before the end of the year.

I tried to draw him out as to how he felt the end might affect us. But although we skirted around the various ways our release could come, like some of the other men, he was withdrawn and cagey. The only cheerful note one could get was from Baldy-Balls-Up who, flapping his large, now bony hands, would laugh airily and sing the camp song, 'Sail Away' – 'That's how it's going to be!'

The skies were battered with heavy dark clouds rumbling explosively most days. The rain dodged about in short heavy showers. The outlook for a late typhoon was prophesied. The cooks begged us to hold on to what Red Cross food stuff we might have saved; there could be a cut in rations. What rations? we quipped. Also we were given continuous reminders to avoid incidents, with either the guards or each other! The pudding was not to be stirred.

Hot steamy weeks bathed the camp in a state of sullen discontent. Postcards and allowances stopped – only temporary, soothed the authorities. We hardly even bothered to crowd round the notice board. Any statements were just old hat. Mother continued to mutter imprecations as to what Mr Churchill would do to the monsters.

This was a bad patch in the camp. We needed a booster – the lack of news from the POW camps across the harbour was frightening. The lack of allowances did not matter because there was nothing to spend them on; even the Blacks were going through a minor depression. This was the one silver lining certainly on Baldy's horizon – he still croaked out the twice daily menu, which was getting briefer each day!

Towards the end of July came the stark and numbing notice from Up-The-Hill. It read, in effect, that the British people had turned their backs on their brilliant leader. Churchill had lost the election. He was OUT. There was an addition to the notice issued, which read 'that this was the greatest error amongst the many that the British people had made and would surely lead to the Allies being vanquished.'

Our committee knew the truth of this. The rest of us refused to accept it, believing it was just another piece of vile propaganda to drown our morale. Even so, most of the ginger was knocked out of us. The daily greeting of 'Hi, Zombie' failed to raise more than a feeble grin. Joyce mentioned one morning in the library in a matter of fact tone, that quite a few of the senior citizens were visiting the office more frequently than in the past. An omen? Of what? We paid little attention. The next observation came from Tom, who said that the Gendarmerie had been seen to evacuate their quarters. This sounded like the real stuff – but what bunch of zombies would take their place?

We limped into August, with the heat and humidity relentless. The sea had lost much of its charm since the sighting of the shark. Even the library customers had dropped off. Joyce asked me to hold the fort, as her mother had had a bad night. She was feverish, complaining of a frightful headache, so Joyce was going down to the hospital to get some aspirin to relieve the pain. A few of the bungalow dwellers gathered round the book-bar for a break from the outside temperature. One of the lads mentioned that from their bungalow they had watched a lot of unusual moving around the Japanese headquarters. 'Looks as if they are either changing staff, or moving out.' Taunts of 'rumour monger' and raucous laughter greeted his observation.

Mentioning this to Rick and Tony that night when we were swapping the day's events, they asked me from which bungalow the chap came, and to repeat what he had said. Had he enlarged on this snippet of information? 'Didn't get a chance, the interest was just rude laughter.' Phil came by at that moment to say that roll-call had been cancelled for the next day. He looked a bit distrait, saying he would like to see

Rick and Tony in his room later.

Suki joined me, looking very weary after her afternoon session in the maternity ward. She had managed to get a few aspirins, having seen Joyce in the morning going down to collect for Mama-T, Suki thought a few extra might be useful. She was looking thin and downcast – obviously the lack of news of her precious Jimmy was really worrying her. She realised how vulnerable the ships were and that some were battened down in the Kowloon Docks. If so, why no news of Jimmy? When it was suitably dark, we made our way down the slope to deliver the aspirin and have a visit with Peg. Suki too, had heard odd bits of conversation between the medicos. Perhaps we would see Tom, who might be able to sort the stories out.

Mama-T was much more comfortable, but Joyce said she wouldn't join us at Peg's. Quite a number of chums were sitting about outside, trying to breathe in some sea breezes. We noticed, too, there were several groups of men bunched together in front of the buildings. They all looked as if they were listening to a lecture. Peg was on the back stoop with Tom, Sid and Jan squatting round her. Our welcome was not as effusive as normal; we both had the feeling that we were interrupting a secret meeting. However, after a few seconds everyone relaxed. Tom explained that owing to the war news, most of the men were being briefed by our committee to stand by for orders.

We mere females were completely confused. What news, what orders, when? The boys made soothing noises, neatly sliding over our questions. They suggested it would be wise to return to our block, as the movements of the guards was very uncertain these last few days. Sid saw us safely up the slope, having cut across the road Suki let out her shrill whistle to

Sid, our safety sign. We then went in search of another discussion group.

The next few days went by in a fever of disorganisation. Ration lorries were late, disrupting the work forces and kitchen staffs. Blockheads advised that certainly the children should be kept away from the beach. Even the weather matched the mood of the camp. Bright hot sunshine part of the day, then broken up by lowering clouds, a light drizzle, or heavy showers. We seemed to be on a perpetual see-saw.

The camp was choking with rumours and tales of so-and-so heard from so-and-so. The fishing fleet had completely deserted their anchorage. There was hardly any movement along the main turning point from the hill into the village road. The reports were that the barracks above our beach was deserted. Yet there was no confirmation officially of any untoward happenings. The seesaw bumped hard on the ground. There was definitely hysteria lurking very close to the surface, but the watchword was to calm down and carry on normally.

Normally? What was that? All the happenings and non-happenings, such as no rations, no regular guards, haphazard roll-calls – it was now like living with *Alice Through the Looking Glass* – except even less believable!

# 16

August 16 – a never to be forgotten date! At last the wondrous news we had all prayed for over the last three and a half years! The unbelievably practical announcement was made by each blockhead to his 'family'. It was early evening when we were summoned to hear 'official news from our President'. Phil, standing on a chair, his face shining with happiness, emotionally read the edict. 'The war is over. The Japanese have surrendered!' *WE WERE FREE*. Just like that! Within moments the camp was reverberating with yells, cheering, and booming voices of 'God Save The King'. Phil held up his hands, as must have the other bearers of this fantastic news. An automatic silence hushed the block. Then we were told that the President begged us to stay in our areas, and to celebrate as calmly as possible until his next bulletin was issued the next morning! Hallelujah! How calmly is possible?

We tried our utmost to remember the discipline of the past years, but it was a wild night of joyous celebration. The piano in St Stephens was heard banging away all the patriotic tunes. Uproarious singing, rushing round hugging and howling! Our only claim to fame was that we did, for the most part, obey the 'order' to remain in our areas. We were much too excited and jubilant to spoil the taste of this night by courting a disaster. Mother's first remark after she had let her breath out was: 'And what did I tell you? No Britisher would ever turn their back on our Churchill.'

As the evening darkened, the lights of the camp shone confidently. Only a few people bothered to note that Up-The-Hill was in comparative and sinister darkness. No one wanted to go to sleep for fear of waking up to find this was all a fantasy. What had brought about the peaceful chain of events we would hear soon enough. Now, this night was for dreaming and planning. Our kitchens were set to go, the staff kept at their posts filling mugs, tins and an assortment of crockery with boiling water for the tea ceremony.

We could hear the firecrackers in the village. Our Chinese fleet were back and celebrating too. The cacophony of their celebrations partnered our own. Quite a few cellars of rice wine were breached and the trumpeting of happy voices sounded far into the morning. Most of us fell into our beds out of physical and mental exhaustion. Mother, for the very first time, sallied out after dark! She crossed over to the American quarters with a pot full of hot strong tea laced with her last bar of wong tong, to celebrate with one of the widows who had become a particular friend of hers!

August 17 – The day of revelation. It was an uneasy and eerie feeling to leave quarters with narry a guard in sight. No roll-call. Notices would be posted on the board about the arrangements for our release and reunion with our men across the harbour. Tedium, monotony and heartbreak so long endured were speedily put aside. We were told that we must remain

264

in camp until the fleet heading towards us at full speed formally took over. A flotilla whose flagship, *Swiftsure,* carrying Admiral Harcourt under the command of Captain Maclaughlin, was on its way from Australia for the surrender of the Japanese and rescue of Hong Kong, the mainland, Kowloon and the New Territories. The exhilaration of awaking free banished the anxiety and heartbreak we had suffered.

In the meantime the essential service left for their posts in the city, where their former Chinese colleagues would join them. Andrew was one of the chaps needed. Before he left he came to tell us an amusing anecdote. Apparently, when our President was given the news by Tanaka of the surrender, Tanaka asked for a police guard from the camp until he could be escorted to Victoria. He feared that he might be attacked by members of the camp. It was quietly explained to him that we were all too busy planning our tomorrows to be interested in our former chief's today.

Rations continued to arrive. News had been received that supplies of food and medicines would be dropped by parachute within the camp. Therefore, we must remain indoors during the drops. The supplies would be retrieved by a team selected by the committee for distribution.

The POWs also had orders to remain in their camps. Their commandant would arrange for groups of them to visit their families by truck as soon as possible. The first truck full of camp relatives arrived, after Nature's typhoon delay. Everyone lined the route hopefully. There were happy reunions and tearful disappointments. The next truck, the unlucky ones felt, my chap will be here.

Another day of rejoicing and thanksgiving. Services were held throughout camp. Our own Church of England padre, and Father Myer of the Jesuits conducted the prayers. Mother wanted to be at the Roman Catholic early service which was being held near the TB sanatorium, to give the patients a chance of joining in. Peg was already there when we arrived, her little puss-cat face grinning with gratefulness. All the services were packed. They continued through the day. It would seem that until this miracle most of us had not bothered or had found it difficult to remember there was a God.

Tom and his syndicate had gone into the city to help with the reconstruction of the administration. They promised to be back for the flag-raising ceremony. Dr Stuart, too, said he would return, bringing Rosie with him.

A number of people with Chinese and Portuguese friends, still in their own homes, had gone to join them. The King Pin and his deputy had flown the coop, with no farewells! What goods remained with the various Blacks were handed over to the office.

The promised parachutes came floating down majestically, carrying their bounty. It was a breathtaking sight, as each morning the packages landed on target. Volunteers came forward to help in the kitchens, to feed the hungry mob!

One of the more fascinating drops was a load of boxes labelled 'K Rations'. The contents looked rather uninteresting. However, we were told it was a type of 'survival kit' for the field – full of vitamins, etc. Ungratefully our fickle nature yearned for the good old tins we could remember from our Red Cross parcels of bully beef, consensed milk and such like. One rapacious character made quite certain that from now on starvation diet was off! The Pasha's room-mates, who had been savouring their new-won freedom like the rest of us, didn't pay much attention to him or his long-hoarded treasure. They teased him a bit, but as he was always most uncooperative and disinterested in what was going on around him, were not undully disturbed when he wandered off by himself, loaded down with his various boxes. When one of them, returning late that evening, found he was not in his usual position on his camp bed, guarding his goods, they thought Rick had better be alerted in case the old boy had got lost in the bushes! That he had. Unbelievable as it sounded – but in fact it was accepted quite matter of factly – he was found dead of over-eating. The first casualty of over-nourishment! Although most of us were taken aback at the cause of death, callously no one mourned him. Poor fellow. The cemetery, we hoped, had claimed its final victim, No. 152.

During the early hours of the following morning the first freedom baby was born in camp. She was the fifty-first in our hospital, but the first to be able to enjoy a normal life. She had the privilege of being given a silk parachute which we hoped would be used to make her christening robe! Although the hospital had been evacuated officially, Dr Stuart had left a skeleton staff to look after the convalescents, who were not really in need of medical care. The serious cases had been hastily taken to the Polfulham Hospital. Roma, the new baby's mother, could have gone into the government hospital at Polfulham, but she chose to have the child in Stanley Camp Hospital. Both Roma and her husband Jack said the baby would be a symbol of God's compassion in keeping their little family safe, their faith which had steadily grown through the years, and the wonderful companionship which had helped sustain them.

Most of our group were still in camp, awaiting repatriation orders. It was the most stimulating time. Chinese friends came to visit, bringing garments they thought might be useful and news of what was happening in town. Messages came from the boys already out, like Tom.

We managed to keep some semblance of routine, such as meals! Most of the nights were spent discussing the final exodus. The next truck with the men with families was due. Joyce's mother and mine were sure our two chaps would be amongst them. We were up and scrubbed by the crack of dawn, with all the other wives and mothers, lining the route to the main gate. The truck was sighted, a crescendo of cheering blasted the air. Names were shouted, the men practically hurled themselves off the truck. Our prayers were answered! Our two chaps were there!

It was heart bursting to see David. He didn't look too much thinner, but as Mother said he was naturally of the greyhound breed! He crushed us both in his arms. I felt as if I was going to do the good old-fashioned swoon! Joyce, Mama-T and John joined us. Young John looked painfully thin but told us how all the friends in the camp had helped to add to his rations – he was the youngest lad in camp, so they all took a fatherly interest in him. Tony came to meet David and said he had vacated his 'suite', for however long we would like to be alone to have a good chat. He had also laid on a chattie with water to boil for a 'cuppa char'. He was so kind and thoughtful. We did not have too long as there was a curfew – and the trucks had to be back over the harbour with their passengers before dark.

It was a full day. So much to talk about, and then we had to show them off to our special friends, all of whom loaded us down with tasty snacks to munch through the short time the chaps were with us. I remembered some time in the garbled conversation to ask if David had received 'the portrait'. He said, 'Best Christmas gift ever. By the time it came PCs had been stopped, so couldn't let you know – great! Everyone loved it.'

David explained to me that the regiment were getting together as soon as possible to find premises to which Mother and I would be taken. For the moment we would have to remain in camp. Nothing could daunt this glorious meeting. Anyway I realised that there was much to be done for his men first. We still had plenty of friends in camp, and glory, we were FREE!

On the formal hand-over to the fleet, the order of evacuation as evaluated by our authorities was obviously the sensible one. Medical cases would come out first; emergencies would be flown either to the UK or Australia, wherever their families were, the rest by sea to the place of their choice between the two countries. As there were only three Indian Army internees, our Regimental Commanding Officer would take care of us!

Where was this rescue fleet? We began to get restive. The enormity of the reorganisation outside our tiny world seemed to elude us. More visits were promised from the now ex-POWs. The weather was breaking, and Rick and Janie suggested that we take our meal down to the beach for a picnic before the storm which was threatening us broke. We lay about luxuriating in this fairy tale come true. Derek and Josie joined us, looking blissful. A young lad from one of the bungalows waved to us as he made for the rocks, we didn't ask him to join us, he had always been a bit of a loner. It was heaven to know we didn't have to slink back, or drag buckets slopping along the route. Rick and Janie were saying that they thoroughly approved of my husband, whom of course they had not met before his visit to camp, and we were teasing Derek and Josie about how soon we could expect to be godparents.

There was a startled fearful scream from the rocks. Simon, the loner, seemed to be in difficulties, half in and half out of the sea, his hands scrabbling at the rocks. The water was churning around him, it was pink. Rick and Derek scrambled through the sand yelling for Simon to hang on. We three watched, sick with horror, as the arms disappeared into a darker pink-foamed sea. Simon was being dragged further and further along the rock line. Then he was gone even before Rick and Derek had heaved themselves up the rocks.

Rick and Derek came back from the rocks, exhausted, their desperation appalling. 'Josie, go to the hospital quickly for a stretcher,' Derek gasped out, through the bile he was bringing up. The three of us raced up the steps, Josie taking the short cut to the hospital. We knew it was too late. The shark had got his first victim. The ghastly tragedy of Simon's terrible death, on top of the fact that it should have happened NOW, as he was to have been flown home from his camp ordeal that evening, was appalling.

Janie and I clung to each other against the jail wall, unable to face going back to the camp with the terrible picture still clear in our minds. Two stretcher bearers raced passed us. We waited, shaking and retching. A menacing, bloated, dark cloud hung overhead. After an age, squatting against the wall, the four lonely figures appeared, the stretcher rolled up, empty.

That night the storm started to build up. Loud far off rumblings of thunder, then slashes of lightning. Rick had reported the accident. We stayed together through most of the night. The next morning the typhoon warning was given out. It was ironical that the 'rescue' mission by the fleet was delayed by our rogue typhoon for two days.

She was a real bitch. But her fury was no greater than ours. How close was the fleet? How long before the calm again?

To be able to get occasional glimpses of those magnificent 'men of war' through the torrential rain was truly a quirk of fate.

August 30. A clear innocent morning. A whoop of recognition from our headland! The fleet could be seen cutting their way past our peninsula. A couple of hardies launched themselves into the sea hoping to reach the proud ships. The master junk set out too, to escort the fleet into the harbour, the junk's green flag stiff in the breeze. She picked up the two chaps clawing through the seas and was off.

Guy had sent out a warning to 'Please do not mar this day by trying to reach the fleet by sea – it will be fatal.' Dozens of the sampans took off to follow the master junk. The seas were still vicious although the sky was a gleaming bright blue with just the odd fluff of white cloud that had got left behind when the typhoon had exhausted herself and us.

Naturally we were all most anxious for news – but, as Guy pointed out, the fleet had to get into harbour and anchor, etc., before we could expect anything concrete.

Guy had been in charge of the camp since the President left to take up his duties in town. That morning he was beleagured in the office by spokesmen for the rest of us, asking for the latest information. Guy himself was waiting anxiously for a directive from the fleet, as to the next move. There was a fervour of anticipation. We were all milling about restlessly, not giving a thought to the fact that we were just one of the tremendous problems to be dealt with. Phil had gone into town with the other men on essential services. Rick was acting for him.

On the evening of August 30, Guy released the message from the fleet. Supplies would be sent in the following day. There would be an officer to represent the Allies' victory at the flag-raising ceremony. This momentous occasion was set for four o'clock that day. The pole was already in position opposite the camp office. Guy had wisely chosen one of the remaining members of the community, a naval officer from the 1918 war, to have the honour of hoisting our flag.

It was unbelievable that the fleet could act so swiftly, but they were obviously aware that we were patiently awaiting our moment of glory when we were to raise our own flag. The 'poached egg' had been torn down immediately we had got the confirmation the war was really over. So the camp was agog, getting things spruced up as much as we could for the visit. It was a privilege to invite the elder of the village to join us in the flag-raising ceremony, also for the kids to come along. They in turn invited any of us who would like to be their guests at a Chinese dinner. That was something that our little coven could not refuse. The elder came plainly dressed so as not to outshine us. Our volunteer cooks had ordered a suitable array of fruit, cakes, biscuits and lots of soft drinks from town. Unfortunately the naval party had to return to their ships. One could imagine how much there was to be done in the next few weeks.

Another night of celebration followed. Somewhere along the line, during our wait for the official relief of the camp, a group from each community had been issued with a supply of miniature bottles of liqueurs. We could only presume that they had come from a cache of the Blacks' provisions. No one had paid any attention to them but tonight it was decided to pool resources for as long as the hooch lasted and have one glorious binge! A good idea in theory but in practice our tummies were uncooperative to this alien diet. There were some sorry-looking specimens lined up the next morning for the arrival of our gallant rescuers!

Lookouts were posted along the route to watch for the motorcade at the turn into Stanley peninsula. There was a curious tension amongst us – almost as though no one really believed this longed-for day was actually going to happen. Then, clearly through the strangely still air, the whistle signalling the approach of the line of cars sent the message through. The cheering spread wildly down the route. Kids broke ranks, swarming into the main road, affected by the gala atmosphere. Then they were there, a cavalcade of vehicles, some of which we had never seen before – jeeps. As they came slowly to a stop opposite the obvious welcoming committee, the younger children shrieked in terror at the sight of these monsters and their personnel – whose startling white uniforms on very large men looked like people from another planet – as indeed they were. We had forgotten how normally nourished human beings looked!

Out of the leading jeep stepped a towering figure

bedecked in gold braid. Guy, thin and somewhat bent in his washed out un-ironed shorts and shirt, returned the salute, introducing himself. As they shook hands his voice was loud and firm as he made the understatement of that day: 'Welcome to Stanley Camp.' As promised, Dr Stuart and Rosie were there with Blossom holding firmly to Rosie's hand, and who with solemn dignity introduced herself! Everyone was eager to help unload the jeeps. The noise was thundering, the children swarming round the sailors who were handing out sweeties. Suddenly, through the cheering and laughter, a woman's voice screamed with delight, 'Look, oh look, they've brought KOTEX.' (These were sanitary towels. Imagine calling those a much needed luxury in earlier days!)

The remainder of the day was chaotic. Questions, questions, the men and boys climbing in and examining these wonderful machines. Smiling crews explained their function and gave rides tirelessly to the young. The time until the great moment of four o'clock arrived passed in a blur of euphoria. Most of us were thoroughly exhausted when called to the ceremony to mark the real moment of truth, our historic moment, the raising of our flag.

Making our way to the already crowded surroundings of the camp office there was hardly time to linger over the memories that collided in the mind: the snippets of good news for myself and friends that came out of that administration office, the smiling face of a colleague, the frightening summonses on orders from Up-The-Hill, to appear before the captor, the dreary days when disastrous happenings to our men and Allies in Europe and the Pacific could not be held from us. Slowly we merged into patterns of families or friends. Most of us already had unashamed tears mingling with our perspiring faces. Somewhere a bugle called hauntingly and a clear firm voice led off with the anthem. It was then that the spell of unreality broke. As we all joined in the singing, the Union Jack sailed majestically to the masthead.

As we watched the much loved red, white and blue emblem of Freedom dance in light afternoon breeze, once more the promise of protection and pride, a palpable quiet gripped the whole camp, as if pre-arranged, to allow emotions to absorb the fact that this was the MOMENT, the culmination of the three years, eight months and sixteen days awaiting the promise we had never really forgotten – THE PROMISE OF FREEDOM.